STRONG-INTERACTION PHYSICS

Frontiers in Physics *A Lecture Note and Reprint Series*

DAVID PINES, *Editor*

P. W. Anderson **CONCEPTS IN SOLIDS:** *Lectures on the Theory of Solids*

N. Bloembergen **NUCLEAR MAGNETIC RELAXATION:** *A Reprint Volume*

Geoffrey F. Chew **S-MATRIX THEORY OF STRONG INTERACTIONS:** *A Lecture Note and Reprint Volume*

R. P. Feynman **QUANTUM ELECTRODYNAMICS:** *A Lecture Note and Reprint Volume*

R. P. Feynman **THE THEORY OF FUNDAMENTAL PROCESSES:** *A Lecture Note Volume*

Hans Frauenfelder **THE MÖSSBAUER EFFECT:** *A Collection of Reprints with an Introduction*

S. C. Frautschi **REGGE POLES & S-MATRIX THEORY:** *A Lecture Note Volume*

Murray Gell-Mann and Yuval Ne'eman **THE EIGHTFOLD WAY**

Robert Hofstadter **NUCLEAR AND NUCLEON STRUCTURE:** *A Reprint Volume*

Maurice Jacob and Geoffrey F. Chew **STRONG-INTERACTION PHYSICS:** *A Lecture Note Volume*

Leo P. Kadanoff and Gordon Baym **QUANTUM STATISTICAL MECHANICS:** *A Lecture Note Volume*

A. M. Lane **RECENT DEVELOPMENTS IN NUCLEAR THEORY:** *A Lecture Note and Reprint Volume*

P. Nozières **THEORY OF INTERACTING FERMI SYSTEMS:** *An Introductory Monograph*

R. Omnès and M. Froissart **MANDELSTAM THEORY AND REGGE POLES:** *An Introduction for Experimentalists*

George E. Pake **PARAMAGNETIC RESONANCE:** *An Introductory Monograph*

David Pines **THE MANY-BODY PROBLEM:** *A Lecture Note and Reprint Volume*

E. J. Squires **COMPLEX ANGULAR MOMENTA AND PARTICLE PHYSICS:** *A Lecture Note and Reprint Volume*

L. Van Hove, N. M. Hugenholtz, and L. P. Howland **PROBLEMS IN THE QUANTUM THEORY OF MANY-PARTICLE SYSTEMS:** *A Reprint Volume*

STRONG-INTERACTION PHYSICS

A LECTURE NOTE VOLUME

MAURICE JACOB
Saclay

GEOFFREY F. CHEW
University of California

W. A. BENJAMIN, INC.
NEW YORK   AMSTERDAM
1964

STRONG-INTERACTION PHYSICS
A Lecture Note Volume

Library of Congress Catalog Card Number 64-21228
Manufactured in the United States of America

The final manuscript was put into production on December 31, 1963;
this volume was published on September 15, 1964

W. A. BENJAMIN, INC.
New York, New York 10016

EDITOR'S FOREWORD

The problem of communicating in a coherent fashion the recent developments in the most exciting and active fields of physics seems particularly pressing today. The enormous growth in the number of physicists has tended to make the familiar channels of communication considerably less effective. It has become increasingly difficult for experts in a given field to keep up with the current literature; the novice can only be confused. What is needed is both a consistent account of a field and the presentation of a definite "point of view" concerning it. Formal monographs cannot meet such a need in a rapidly developing field, and, perhaps more important, the review article seems to have fallen into disfavor. Indeed, it would seem that the people most actively engaged in developing a given field are the people least likely to write at length about it.

"Frontiers in Physics" has been conceived in an effort to improve the situation in several ways. First, to take advantage of the fact that the leading physicists today frequently give a series of lectures, a graduate seminar, or a graduate course in their special fields of interest. Such lectures serve to summarize the present status of a rapidly developing field and may well constitute the only coherent account available at the time. Often, notes on lectures exist (prepared by the lecturer himself, by graduate students, or by postdoctoral fellows) and have been distributed in mimeographed form on a limited basis. One of the principal purposes of the "Frontiers in Physics" series is to make such notes available to a wider audience of physicists.

It should be emphasized that lecture notes are necessarily rough and informal, both in style and content, and those in the series will prove no exception. This is as it should be. The point of the series is to offer new, rapid, more informal, and, it is hoped, more effective ways for physicists to teach one another. The point is lost if only elegant notes qualify.

A second way to improve communication in very active fields of physics is by the publication of collections of reprints of recent articles. Such collections are themselves useful to people working in the field. The value of the reprints would, however, seem much enhanced if the collection would be accompanied by an introduction of moderate length, which would serve to tie the collection together and, necessarily, constitute a brief survey of the present status of the field. Again, it is appropriate that such an introduction be informal, in keeping with the active character of the field.

A third possibility for the series might be called an informal monograph, to connote the fact that it represents an intermediate step between lecture notes and formal monographs. It would offer the author an opportunity to present his views of a field that has developed to the point at which a summation might prove extraordinarily fruitful, but for which a formal monograph might not be feasible or desirable.

Fourth, there are the contemporary classics—papers or lectures which constitute a particularly valuable approach to the teaching and learning of physics today. Here one thinks of fields that lie at the heart of much of present-day research, but whose essentials are by now well understood, such as quantum electrodynamics or magnetic resonance. In such fields some of the best pedagogical material is not readily available, either because it consists of papers long out of print or lectures that have never been published.

"Frontiers in Physics" is designed to be flexible in editorial format. Authors are encouraged to use as many of the foregoing approaches as seem desirable for the project at hand. The publishing format for the series is in keeping with its intentions. Photo-offset printing is used throughout, and the books are paperbound, in order to speed publication and reduce costs. It is hoped that the books will thereby be within the financial reach of graduate students in this country and abroad.

Finally, because the series represents something of an experiment on the part of the editor and the publisher, suggestions from interested readers as to format, contributors, and contributions will be most welcome.

David Pines

Urbana, Illinois
August 1961

PREFATORY NOTE

This volume brings together two short graduate courses on strong interactions given in the Middle East Technical University, Ankara, during the academic year 1962–63.

The first course, by Dr. Maurice Jacob, covers the phenomenological aspects of pion-nucleon interactions and is designed to introduce, at a fairly elementary level, current mathematical methods for analyzing strong collision processes and to familiarize the reader with the use of some calculational techniques by means of simple examples.

The second course, by Professor Geoffrey F. Chew, is devoted to the exposition of the main ideas and concepts of the S-matrix theory, which treats all strongly interacting particles (including resonances) on the same footing. Attempts are being made to put the S-matrix theory on an independent postulational basis. Whether such postulates turn out to be ultimately derivable from local field theory or not, this effort seems to be well motivated, since some conjectures about the analytic properties of the S-matrix, together with such well-established principles as Lorentz invariance and unitarity, have permitted us to correlate an impressive body of experimental data in the domain of strong interactions. In these lectures Professor Chew argues effectively for an independent S-matrix theory for strongly interacting particles with a new emphasis on "bootstrap dynamics," a self-consistency requirement for particle and resonant states and the forces they exert on each other.

The introductory and illustrative character of the two courses should be apparent to the reader: strange-particle physics is almost completely omitted and the unitary symmetry of the strongly interacting particles is merely alluded to. The empirical fact that perturbation calculations appear to describe usefully the departures from SU_3 symmetry poses a tantalizing question about the possible existence and origin of small dimensionless numbers within the framework of "nuclear democracy." Whether the unitary symmetry itself can arise from a self-consistency requirement for the multitude of strongly interacting particles is another open question.

It is hoped that the lectures presented here will prove helpful and stimulating to those physicists who would wish to have a background in strong-interaction physics, as new experiments are beginning to hint at a new order in the domain of fundamental processes, including strong, electromagnetic, and weak interactions.

Professor Chew and Professor Jacob came to Ankara under a visiting professorship program made possible through a grant from the Ford Foundation, which assistance is gratefully acknowledged. The program was planned and organized by Professor E. Inönü, Chairman of the Theoretical Physics Department of the Middle East Technical University.

FEZA GÜRSEY

Princeton, New Jersey
April 1964

(Permanent address:
Middle East Technical University
Ankara, Turkey)

CONTENTS

AN INTRODUCTION TO THE ANALYSIS OF STRONG-INTERACTION PROCESSES

PREFACE

This set of notes is the outcome of courses given at the Middle East Technical University in Ankara, Turkey, during the fall of 1962 and at the University of Paris, at Orsay, during the winter 1962-63. They were prepared for graduate students who had already taken a course in Quantum Mechanics and were taking a course in field theory. A similar course was also given at the Institut des Sciences et Techniques Nucléaires at Saclay for experimental physicists working at the Saturne synchrotron.

The purpose of this course was to illustrate, with examples taken from strong interactions, present methods of theoretical analysis of experimental data. It is strongly focussed on pion-nucleon interactions and on the new mesons.

After a review of basic relations following from Lorentz invariance, unitarity, and charge independence, the requirements of rotational invariance, parity conservation, and time reserval invariance for collisions between particles of arbitrary spin are analysed in detail using the helicity formalism. The isotopic spin and G-parity formalisms are presented.

These relations are then applied to the study of the resonances. It is shown how the quantum numbers can be obtained through a phenomenological analysis of the data.

Crossing and analyticity properties of the scattering amplitudes are then introduced as a working hypothesis. The application of forward scattering and fixed momentum transfer dispersion relations to the analysis of pion-nucleon scattering is presented. The determination of the pion-nucleon coupling constant provides an example of the pole extrapolation technique which is then extended to other cases. This leads to the peripherical model and evidence for peripheral interactions are discussed.

MAURICE JACOB

Gif-sur-Yvette, France
April 1964

INTRODUCTION

THE following set of notes is the outcome of courses given at the Middle East Technical University in Ankara, Turkey, during the fall of 1962 and at the Faculté des Sciences de l'Université de Paris at Orsay in the winter 1962–1963. They were prepared for graduate students who, at Orsay or in Ankara, had already taken a course in Quantum Mechanics and were taking a course in Field Theory. This course was also given at the Institut des Sciences et Techniques Nucléaires at Saclay for experimental physicists working at the Saturne synchrotron.

The main purpose of these lectures was to illustrate, with some examples taken from strong-interaction processes, the present methods of theoretical analysis of experimental data. In effect, in connection with research work carried out at Saturne, they were strongly focused on pion-nucleon interactions and almost nothing is said about strong interactions with strange particles.

The notes have been divided into separate chapters. On the average, each chapter contains the material presented during two or three lectures.

Chapters 1 and 2 review the general relations that are used in the analysis of any elementary particle collision. In Chapter 1, the requirements imposed by Lorentz invariance and unitarity on the reaction amplitudes are presented and cross-section formulas are derived. This has not any pretention to be complete. The reader is assumed to be already a little familiar with these notions. The purpose of the first lectures was merely to put together, and illustrate with examples, some basic relations and, by the same token, to define notations. The metric used throughout is such that the modulus squared of a 4-vector reads $p^2 = \mathbf{p}^2 - p_0^2$. Therefore for a free particle we write $p^2 = -M^2$. The Dirac γ-matrices are taken as hermitian. The units used throughout are such that $\hbar = c = 1$. The nucleon and pion masses which often occur in the formulas are, respectively, designated by m and μ.

Chapter 2 deals with the partial-wave expansion of center-of-mass amplitudes for two-body reactions. The requirements of rotational invariance, parity conservation, and time reversal invariance for collisions between particles of arbitrary spin are presented in the helicity formalism. The formulas obtained apply equally well for massless particles. The application to pion-nucleon scattering is then considered in great detail.

Charge independence is then analyzed in the third chapter. The isotopic spin formalism is applied to reactions between nucleons and pions. As in the preceding chapter special attention is paid to pion-nucleon scattering. Then G-parity is discussed, and selection rules are derived for nucleon-antinucleon annihilations and for many-meson reactions.

Chapters 4 and 5 provide an illustration of the formalism developed in the preceding three chapters with an analysis of strong-interaction processes. The field of strong interactions between elementary particles is already wide. Even though we excluded to start with a detailed study of interactions with strange particles, these lectures could not have the pretention to give a comprehensive account of the present understanding of interactions between pions and nucleons. Therefore we have focused them on a discussion of the resonances. Chapter 4 deals with the pion-nucleon resonances and Chapter 5 with the newly discovered mesons. In both chapters we stay on pure phenomenological ground. We show how the relations obtained from general invariance principles can be used to analyze the experimental data.

In Chapter 6, on the other hand, we consider some applications of dispersion relations to pion-nucleon scattering. The crossing properties and the analyticity properties obtained from microcausality in quantum field theory are quoted. The derivation of dispersion relations in the framework of field theory is not given since the text would have departed from its mainly phenomenological character. The reader is referred to "Les Houches Lecture Notes" by M. L. Goldberger and R. Omnès[1] or to the lecture notes by J. D. Jackson.[2]

Crossing symmetry and analyticity properties are introduced as working hypotheses. Fixed, momentum transfer, dispersion relations are written, and some applications are discussed.

Finally, Chapter 7 presents some examples that illustrate the use of nearby singularities. The conjectures leading to the Mandelstam representation are briefly presented. We show how the existence of poles in reaction amplitudes can be used to obtain important quantities through an extrapolation procedure. We also discuss experimental evidence for peripheral interactions.

In its actual version, the course also included a short discussion of the Mandelstam representation. The motivations for the introduction of Regge poles in strong-interaction physics were presented and experimental consequences were discussed. This has been omitted here since this matter is thoroughly discussed in the lecture notes of G. F. Chew.

The reference list given is by no means intended to be a comprehensive one. A reference was quoted whenever a detailed discussion of a particular point mentioned would have been outside the scope of these notes. The papers referred to will provide the reader with a more complete list of references for each particular topic.

It is a pleasure to thank R. Stora and G. Cohen for their help in bringing these notes to their present form.

1

KINEMATICAL GENERALITIES

1–1 SCATTERING AMPLITUDE AND CROSS SECTION

Let us consider an ideal elastic scattering process. A beam of particles with velocities $\mathbf{v} = \mathbf{k}/E$ falls on a target of n scattering centers. We write the incident flux as Nv and assume that each target particle scatters independently. Their distances are supposed to be large compared to the associated wavelength of the incident particles $\lambda\!\!\!^{-} = k^{-1}$. The number of particles scattered per unit time in an elementary solid angle $d\Omega$ in the direction θ, φ (Fig. 1-1) is equal to

$$dn' = Nnv \frac{d\sigma}{d\Omega} d\Omega$$

this defines the differential cross section $d\sigma/d\Omega$. The cross section is

$$\sigma = \int \frac{d\sigma}{d\Omega} d\Omega$$

For inelastic scattering more variables are required to specify the particular final state considered. Partial differential cross sections with respect to these variables are defined in a similar way. Summing over all processes gives the total cross section σ_{tot}.

With such collisions, transitions are observed between states that are to be identified asymptotically as time tends to $\pm\infty$ with free-particle states. It is convenient to define two complete sets of such states in Hilbert space. They are denoted by $|\alpha \text{ in}\rangle$ and $|\beta \text{ out}\rangle$. α and β stand for all the quantum numbers that are necessary to describe completely these states as time tends to $-\infty$ for $|\alpha \text{ in}\rangle$ and as time tends to $+\infty$ for $|\beta \text{ out}\rangle$. Except for the vacuum state and one-particle states,

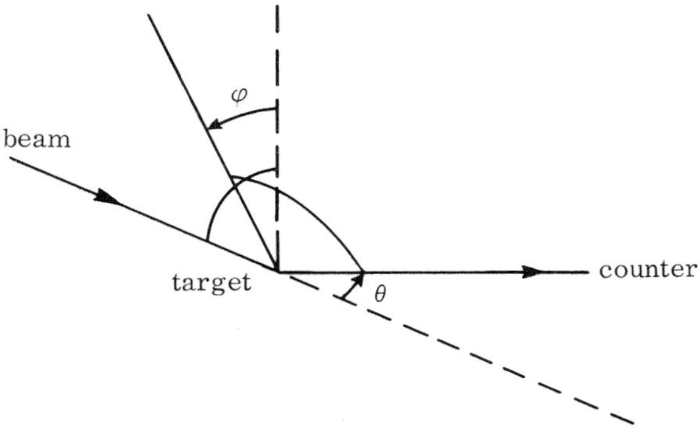

Figure 1-1

$|\alpha \text{ in}\rangle$ and $|\alpha \text{ out}\rangle$ are obviously different states. The transition amplitude between two free-particle states specified by the set of quantum numbers α and β is then the component of $|\alpha \text{ in}\rangle$ on $|\beta \text{ out}\rangle$, namely, $\langle\beta \text{ out}|\alpha \text{ in}\rangle$.

One goes from the "out" base to the "in" base by means of a unitary transformation: the S-matrix

$$S|\beta \text{ out}\rangle = |\beta \text{ in}\rangle \tag{1-1}$$

A transition is then characterized by a particular S-matrix element

$$\langle\beta \text{ out}|\alpha \text{ in}\rangle = \langle\beta \text{ out}|S|\alpha \text{ out}\rangle = S_{\beta\alpha} \tag{1-2}$$

and since S is a unitary operator: $S^{-1} = S^\dagger$

$$\langle\beta \text{ out}| = \langle\beta \text{ in}|S$$

or

$$\langle\beta \text{ out}|\alpha \text{ in}\rangle = \langle\beta \text{ in}|S|\alpha \text{ in}\rangle = S_{\beta\alpha}$$

The T-matrix is defined by the relation

$$S \equiv I + iT \tag{1-3}$$

where I stands for the unit operator.

The modulus squared of T-matrix elements are then closely related to cross sections. In order to obtain the precise connection we first have to specify a normalization for the free-particle states considered.

A one-particle state is fully specified by the momentum $\mathbf{k}$ and a spin component s of the particle. We denote it as $|\mathbf{k},s\rangle$ and choose the normalization

$$\langle \mathbf{k}', s' | \mathbf{k}, s\rangle = \delta_{ss'}(2\pi)^3 \delta(\mathbf{k} - \mathbf{k}') \tag{1-4}$$

with the closure relation

$$\sum_{s'} \int |\mathbf{k}', s'\rangle \langle \mathbf{k}', s' | \mathbf{k}, s\rangle \frac{d^3\mathbf{k}'}{(2\pi)^3} = |\mathbf{k},s\rangle \tag{1-5}$$

Many-particle states are further defined as direct products of such one-particle states. A T-matrix element is written in the following way:

$$T_{fi} = (2\pi)^4 \delta(P_f - P_i) \frac{F_{fi}}{\left(2E_1^i 2E_2^i 2E_1^f 2E_2^f \cdots\right)^{1/2}} \tag{1-6}$$

where P_i (and P_f) is the total momentum, energy vector in the initial (and final) states, and $E_1^i E_2^i$ (and $E_1^f E_2^f \cdots$) are the energies of the initial (and final) particles.

The modulus squared of the T-matrix element with summation over all possible final states and normalization to a unit flux gives the transition probability per unit time and unit incident flux to all states accessible with conservation of total energy and momentum. This is the cross section. The final-state density is obtained from (1-5). It is

$$\Pi_j \frac{d^3\mathbf{k}_j}{(2\pi)^3}$$

where Π_j means a product of terms pertaining to all final particles. In (1-6) the product of twice the energy for all the particles in the initial $(2E_1^i 2E_2^i)$ and final $(2E_1^f 2E_2^f \cdots)$ states appears under a square root in the denominator. It is included so that the amplitude F_{fi} is a Lorentz invariant quantity. This results obviously from the particular normalization chosen in (1-4). F is the amplitude as obtained from Feynman graphs in perturbation theory times a factor $\sqrt{2m}$ for each external fermion line.

Let us first describe a reaction in the laboratory system. One of the initial particles is at rest. The incident flux is simply equal to the velocity of the other one, namely, $|\mathbf{q}_1|/E_1^i$. The cross section reads

$$\sigma = \frac{(2\pi)^4}{4|\mathbf{q}_1| E_2^i} \int \delta(P_i - P_f) |F_{fi}|^2 \Pi_j \frac{d^3\mathbf{k}_j}{(2\pi)^3 2E_j^f} \tag{1-7}$$

It is a Lorentz invariant quantity and the right-hand side can be easily put in an obviously invariant form. $q_1 E_2^i$ is the laboratory variable expression of the invariant quantity $[(q_1 \cdot q_2)^2 - (m_1 m_2)^2]^{1/2}$, where q_1 and q_2 are the initial-particle 4-momenta. Furthermore we can replace $d^3\mathbf{k}_j / 2E_j$ by $d^4 k_j\ \delta(k_j^2 + m_j^2)$ under the integral, retaining only positive energies. We obtain

$$\sigma = \frac{(2\pi)^4}{4\sqrt{(q_1 \cdot q_2)^2 - (m_1 m_2)^2}} \int |F|^2\ \delta\left(q_1 + q_2 - \sum_j k_j\right)$$

$$\times\ \Pi_j\ \Theta\left(k_j^0\right) \delta\left(k_j^2 - m_j^2\right) \frac{d^4 k_j}{(2\pi)^3} \qquad (1\text{-}8)$$

where Θ stands for the step function. From (1-8), differential cross sections in any particular reference frame are easily obtained in terms of the invariant amplitude F. There are a priori as many amplitudes to consider as possible spin states in the initial and final states. This will be discussed in detail later.

1–2 TWO- AND THREE-BODY REACTIONS

As a particular example let us consider a two-body reaction $a + b \to c + d$ in the center-of-mass system

$$(m_1 m_2)^2 - (q_1 \cdot q_2)^2 = (m_1 m_2)^2 - (E_1^2 E_2^2 + 2E_1 E_2 q^2 + q^4)$$

where q is the center-of-mass momentum in the initial state

$$E_1 = \sqrt{q^2 + m^2} \qquad E_2 = \sqrt{q^2 + m_2^2}$$

hence

$$(m_1 m_2)^2 - (q_1 \cdot q_2)^2 = -q^2 (E_1^2 + E_2^2 + 2E_1 E_2) = -q^2 W^2$$

where W is the total center-of-mass energy.

$$\sigma = \frac{1}{16(2\pi)^2 qW} \int \delta\left(\sqrt{p^2 + m_3^2} + \sqrt{p^2 + m_4^2} - W\right)$$

$$\times\ \frac{|F|^2}{E_3 E_4}\ d^3\mathbf{p}$$

where $\mathbf{p}$ is the center-of-mass momentum in the final state. We use the last δ-function to integrate over the modulus of $\mathbf{p}$ and we are left with an integral over the direction of $\mathbf{p}$

$$\sigma = \frac{1}{(8\pi)^2 qW} \int \frac{E_3 E_4}{pW} \frac{|F|^2}{E_3 E_4} p^2 \, d\Omega \tag{1-9}$$

or

$$\frac{d\sigma}{d\Omega} = \frac{p}{q} \left| \frac{F}{8\pi W} \right|^2$$

with $d\Omega = d\cos\theta \, d\varphi$.

For elastic scattering the differential cross section reads

$$\frac{d\sigma}{d\Omega} = \frac{1}{64\pi^2 W^2} |F|^2 \tag{1-10}$$

The scattering angle θ is simply related to the momentum transfer squared $-t$ by $t = -2q^2(1-\cos\theta)$

$$\cos\theta = 1 + \frac{t}{2q^2}$$

One also considers the differential cross section with respect to t

$$\frac{d\sigma}{dt\, d\varphi} = \frac{|F|^2}{128\pi^2 q^2 W^2} \tag{1-11}$$

If F behaves like $s = W^2$ when $s \to \infty$, (1-11) shows that the shape of the elastic scattering pattern with respect to t does not depend asymptotically upon the energy. As shown later (1-25), if the imaginary part of F is larger than its real part, this behavior also leads to a constant, total, cross section at high energies. The converse is not true.

The scattering amplitude in a particular reference frame is usually defined in such a way that

$$\frac{d\sigma}{d\Omega} = |f|^2 \tag{1-12}$$

$F/(8\pi W)$ is the center-of-mass scattering amplitude. It is easy to check that F is equal to the scattering amplitude in the target rest frame times a constant factor $8\pi M$. M is the mass of the target particle.

As a further example let us consider a reaction of the type $a + b \to c + d + e$. By taking center-of-mass variables, we write

$$\sigma = \frac{(2\pi)^4}{32qW} \int \delta(P_i - P_f) \frac{|F|^2}{E_1 E_2 E_3} \frac{d^3\mathbf{p}_1 \, d^3\mathbf{p}_2 \, d^3\mathbf{p}_3}{(2\pi)^9}$$

where $(\mathbf{p}_i, \mathbf{E}_i)$ are the momentum-energy of the three final particles. Let us use the four δ-functions to integrate over $\mathbf{p}_3$ and the cosine of the angle between the vectors $\mathbf{p}_1$ and $\mathbf{p}_2$, x.

$$\sigma = \frac{1}{32qW(2\pi)^5} \times \int \delta\left(\sqrt{p_1^2 + m_1^2} + \sqrt{p_2^2 + m_2^2} + \sqrt{p_1^2 + p_2^2 + 2p_1 p_2 x + m_3^2} - W\right) \times \frac{|F|^2 \, d^3\mathbf{p}_1 p_2^2 \, dp_2 \, d\Omega_2}{E_1 E_2 E_3} \tag{1-13}$$

$$\sigma = \frac{1}{32qW(2\pi)^5} \int |F|^2 \, d\Omega_1 \, d\varphi \, dE_1 \, dE_2$$

with $p\,dp = E\,dE$ and $d\Omega_2 = dx\,d\varphi$.

It is often useful to consider a graphic representation where each event is represented as a point, the coordinates of which are the center-of-mass kinetic energies of two of the final particles $T_1 = E_1 - m_1$ and $T_2 = E_2 - m_2$. Conservation of momentum and energy restricts all the points to be inside a closed curve tangent to both axes $T_1 = 0$, $T_2 = 0$ (Fig. 1-2). This is a Dalitz plot. If F is a constant, (1-13) shows that the density of points is a constant over the Dalitz plot.

On the other hand, if F is not constant, for instance if there is a strong final-state interaction when the center-of-mass energy of two particles, and hence the kinetic energy of the third one, has a particular value, this will show up in a striking way on the Dalitz plot.

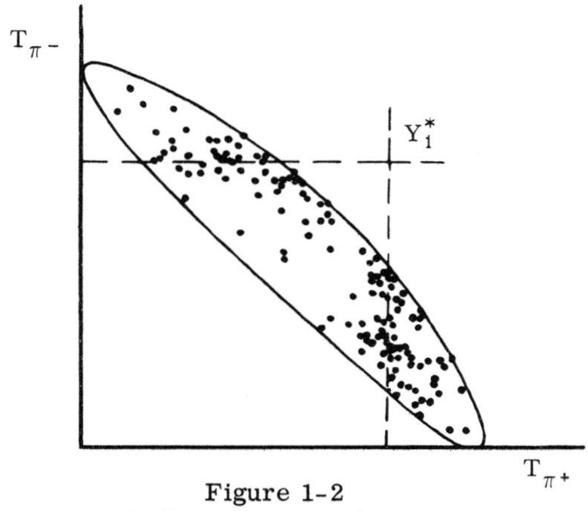

Figure 1-2

$K^- p \rightarrow \Lambda\pi^+\pi^-$ at 1150 MeV/c. There is a strong enhancement when the $\Lambda\pi$ center-of-mass energy is close to 1385 MeV. This corresponds actually to a resonance called Y_1^*.

1–3 DECAY RATES

Decay rates are computed in a very similar way. We take the modulus square of (1-6) summed over all possible final states. The $(4E_1^i E_2^i)^{-1/2}$ factor is replaced by $(2M)^{-1/2}$, where M is the mass of the decaying particle. We obtain the inverse mean life of the particle measured in its rest frame.

As a particular example let us consider the decay of a vector particle into two or three pseudoscalar, equal mass particles.

For the two-body decay the decay amplitude should be a scalar, linear in the polarization vector B. For a spin-1 particle we have $B \cdot k = 0$, where k is the decay-particle momentum. The amplitude is therefore written as

$$F = G_1 B \cdot q \tag{1-14}$$

and G_1 is a function of the kinematical invariants of the decay which are fixed: $k^2 = -M^2$ and $p_1^2 = p_2^2 = -\mu^2$.

The partial decay rate is

$$\Gamma_1 = \frac{G_1^2}{8M}(2\pi)^4 \int \delta(2\sqrt{q^2 + \mu^2} - M) \,|\, B \cdot q \,|^2 \, \frac{q^2\, dq\, d\Omega}{(2\pi)^6 (q^2 + \mu^2)}$$

or

$$\Gamma_1 = \frac{1}{3}\, \frac{G_1^2}{4\pi}\, \frac{(M^2 - 4\mu^2)^{3/2}}{16M^2}$$

For the three-body decay, the decay amplitude to consider is of the form

$$F = G_2\, \epsilon_{\mu\nu\sigma\rho} B^{\mu} p_1^{\nu} p_2^{\sigma} p_3^{\rho} \tag{1-15}$$

since it must be a pseudoscalar quantity linear in the polarization vector. G_2 is now a function of the two, independent, invariant quantities which can be defined from the three independent vectors p_1, p_2, and p_3. (Say $p_1 p_2$ and $p_1 p_3$.) For the sake of simplicity let us assume that G_2 is constant. We then obtain in a straightforward way the corresponding Dalitz plot density. The rate reads

$$\Gamma_2 = \frac{G_2^2}{4\pi}\, \frac{M}{3\pi^2} \int \Big[(\omega_1^2 - \mu^2)(\omega_2^2 - \mu^2)$$

$$- \tfrac{1}{4}[M^2 + \mu^2 - 2M(\omega_1 + \omega_2) + 2\omega_1\omega_2]^2 \Big] \, d\omega_1 \, d\omega_2$$

where ω_1 and ω_2 are the center-of-mass energy of any two of the three particles.

The mean life τ is $\tau = (\Gamma_1 + \Gamma_2)^{-1}$.

1—4 PION-NUCLEON SCATTERING AMPLITUDES

In the two examples we have just considered it is easy to check that the most general forms of the decay amplitudes are, respectively, given by (1-14) and (1-15). In π-nucleon scattering we have a priori many possible scalar amplitudes, such as

$$\bar{u}(p_2)u(p_1) \qquad \bar{u}(p_2)\gamma_\mu u(p_1)q_1^\mu \qquad \bar{u}(p_2)\gamma_\mu u(p_1)q_2^\mu \cdots$$

where $u(p_1)$ [and $u(p_2)$] are the nucleon spinors in the initial (and final) states. We take $\bar{u}u = 1$. q_1 (and q_2), p_1 (and p_2) are, respectively, the momenta of the initial (and final) pion and nucleon.

We shall exhibit later a very simple method to find the number of independent scattering amplitudes in any two-body reaction. For π-nucleon scattering there are only two of them and one usually writes[3]

$$F = -2m\bar{u}(p_2)\left(-A + \frac{iB}{2}\gamma_\mu(q_1 + q_2)^\mu\right)u(p_1) \tag{1-16}$$

A and B are functions of all the independent invariant quantities that can be constructed with the three independent vectors P_1, q_1, and q_2, $(p_1 + q_1 = p_2 + q_2)$. There are only two besides the masses squared. A and B contain all the dynamics, and (1-16) merely takes care of the so-called unessential complications due to the nucleon spin.

Although A and B are Lorentz invariant quantities, it is often more convenient to consider scattering amplitudes in the center-of-mass system. They are simpler since the conservation of momentum and energy is already taken into account.

In the center-of-mass system $\mathbf{p}_1 = -\mathbf{q}_1$, $\mathbf{p}_2 = -\mathbf{q}_2$. We write F as

$$F = \frac{-1}{(E + m)}\bar{\chi}_f(i\gamma p_2 - m)$$

$$\times\left(-A + i\frac{B}{2}\gamma(q_2 + q_2)\right)(i\gamma p_1 - m)\chi_i \tag{1-16'}$$

where χ_i and χ_f are spinors with lower components equal to zero. The subscripts i and f refer to the nucleon spin components in the initial and final states, respectively; E and ω are the nucleon and pion energies, respectively. $E + \omega = W$.

Only the terms with an even power of γ-matrices (we take γ_0 diagonal) contribute to (1-16′). We can then replace the γ-matrices by 2×2 σ-matrices and consider χ as a two-component spinor.

Let us then define two amplitudes f_1 and f_2 by

$$F = 8\pi W \chi_f^\dagger (f_1 + f_2 \sigma \hat{q}_2 \sigma \hat{q}_1) \chi_i \tag{1-17}$$

This is obviously the most general amplitude written in terms of the center-of-mass variables. $\hat{q}$ stands for a unit vector along $\mathbf{q}$. The factor $8\pi W$ has been introduced so that according to (1-9)

$$\frac{d\sigma}{d\Omega} = |\chi_f^\dagger (f_1 + f_2 \sigma \hat{q}_2 \sigma \hat{q}_1) \chi_i|^2 \tag{1-18}$$

f_1 and f_2 are now functions of the center-of-mass quantities W and $\hat{q}_1 \cdot \hat{q}_2$ (or $\cos\theta$). As shown in the next chapter they are simply related to the phase shifts.

We identify (1-16) and (1-17) and obtain

$$\left.\begin{aligned} f_1 &= \frac{E + m}{8\pi W} [A + B(W - m)] \\ f_2 &= \frac{-(E - m)}{8\pi W} [A - B(W + m)] \end{aligned}\right\} \tag{1-19}$$

or

$$A = 4\pi \left[f_1 \frac{W + m}{E + m} - f_2 \frac{W - m}{E - m} \right]$$

$$B = 4\pi \left[\frac{f_1}{E + m} + \frac{f_2}{E - m} \right]$$

The charges of the nucleon and pion have been so far neglected. We have a priori to consider A and B as functions of the charge configuration. The number of independent functions is, however, limited by the charge independence property of strong interactions. This is discussed in detail in Chapter 3.

1–5 KINEMATICAL INVARIANTS

For π-nucleon scattering and for any reaction of the type $a + b \rightarrow c + d$, where there are three independent momenta p_1, p_2, p_3, with $p_1 + p_2 = p_3 + p_4$, we have only two independent invariant quantities (Fig. 1-3). A convenient choice is to take[4]

$$\left.\begin{aligned} s &= -(p_1 + p_2)^2 = -(p_3 + p_4)^2 \\ t &= -(p_1 - p_3)^2 = -(p_2 - p_4)^2 \end{aligned}\right\} \tag{1-20a}$$

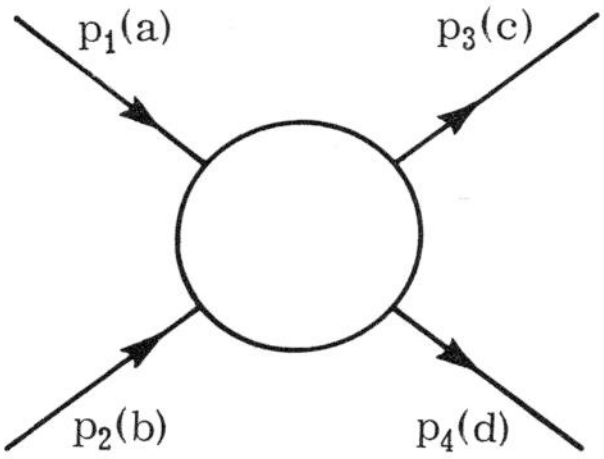

Figure 1-3

s is the square of the center-of-mass energy, $s = W^2$, and $-t$ is the square of the momentum transfer between particles a and c (or b and d). For elastic scattering, t has a simple expression in terms of the center-of-mass variables q^2 and $\cos\theta$.

$$t = -2q^2(1 - \cos\theta)$$

To preserve the symmetry between the four momenta, a third invariant quantity is also considered together with s and t,

$$u = -(p_1 - p_4)^2 = -(p_2 - p_3)^2 \tag{1-20b}$$

where $-u$ is the square of the momentum transfer between particles a and d (or b and c). s, t, and u are not independent. It is easy to check that

$$s + t + u = m_1^2 + m_2^2 + m_3^2 + m_4^2 \tag{1-21}$$

s, t, and u describe the reaction $a + b \to c + d$ and the time-reversed one. They can be used as well to describe other reactions if we formally replace an incoming particle of momentum p by an outgoing antiparticle of momentum $-p$, and an outgoing particle by an incoming antiparticle of opposite momentum. If we consider the reaction $\bar{c} + b \to \bar{a} + d$ ($\bar{a}$ is the antiparticle of a), the initial (and final) momenta are denoted, respectively, $-p_3$ and p_2 (and $-p_1$, p_4), and the center-of-mass energy squared is now given by u. $-s$ is the momentum transfer squared between $\bar{c}$ and d; $-t$ is the momentum transfer squared between $\bar{c}$ and $\bar{a}$. Going from one reaction to the other we exchange the role of s and u; t keeps the same role.

In a similar way if we consider the reaction $a + \bar{c} \to \bar{b} + d$ the initial momenta are p_1 and $-p_3$. The center-of-mass energy squared is equal to t. The role of s and t have now been interchanged. The role of u remains unchanged.

Each reaction corresponds, however, to particular values of s, t,

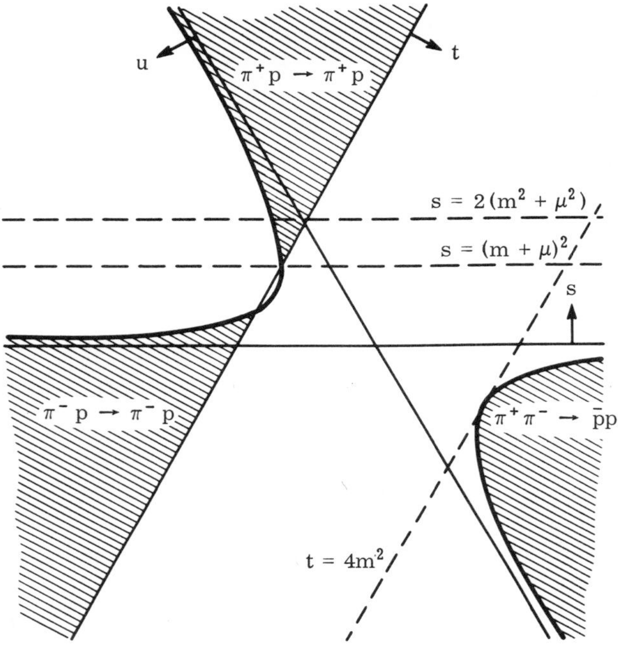

Figure 1-4

and u with no overlap. This is illustrated by Fig. 1-4 for the particular case of π-nucleon scattering. Each event is shown as a point on a triangular graph. The distances to the sides of an equilateral triangle are equal to s, t, and u with $s + t + \mu = 2(m^2 + \mu^2)$. The first reaction is, for instance, $\pi^+ + p \to \pi^+ + p$. It corresponds to $s \geq (m + \mu)^2$, $t \leq 0$, and $u \leq (m^2 - \mu^2)^2/s$. This defines the physical region for this particular reaction. We now exchange the incoming π^+ with an outgoing π^-, and vice versa s and u are exchanged. The physical region for the new reaction is now defined by

$$u \geq (m + \mu)^2 \qquad t \leq 0 \qquad \text{and} \qquad s \leq \frac{(m^2 - \mu^2)^2}{u}$$

Finally we can interchange the outgoing π^+ with an incoming π^- and the incoming proton with an outgoing antiproton. This is the reaction $\pi^+\pi^- \to p\bar{p}$. It corresponds to $t \geq 4m^2$. t is the center-of-mass energy squared for this reaction. The physical region is limited by the other branch of the hyperbola (Fig. 1-4).

In perturbation theory the same functions A(s,t,u) and B(s,t,u) would describe all three reactions. The same graphs will serve to calculate all three processes. This result is valid independently of perturbation theory and is known as crossing symmetry. Nevertheless, it is a powerful statement only if it is possible to define an analytic continuation of the scattering amplitudes from one physical region to the other. This will be discussed later.

1–6 UNITARITY RELATION AND OPTICAL THEOREM

The unitarity property of the S-matrix provides useful relations among the scattering amplitudes. Following (1-3) and (1-6), an S-matrix element is written

$$S_{fi} = \delta_{fi} + i(2\pi)^4\ \delta(P_f - P_i)M_{fi} \tag{1-22}$$

By using (1-22) together with the unitarity relation

$$(SS^\dagger)_{fi} = \sum_n S_{fn} S^*_{in} = \delta_{fi} \tag{1-23}$$

where Σ_n stands for a summation over all possible states accessible from the initial state, we obtain the unitarity relation in terms of the M-matrix:

$$i\left(M_{fi} - M^*_{if}\right) = -(2\pi)^4 \sum_n \delta(P_i - P_n)M_{fn} M^*_{in} \tag{1-24}$$

All matrix elements correspond to actual physical processes. As a simple example let us consider a two-body reaction and assume that all accessible states consist of two spinless, equal mass, particles ($\pi\pi$ scattering below threshold for the $2\pi \rightarrow 4\pi$ reaction). Taking center-of-mass variables we obtain

$$i\left(F_{fi} - F^*_{if}\right) = -(2\pi)^4 \int \frac{F_{fn} F^*_{in}}{W^2}\ \delta(P_i - P_n)\ \frac{d^3\mathbf{k}_1\ d^3\mathbf{k}_2}{(2\pi)^6}$$

or

$$-i\left(F_{fi} - F^*_{if}\right) = \frac{1}{(2\pi)^2}\ \frac{\sqrt{(W^2/4) - \mu^2}}{4W} \int F_{fn} F^*_{in}\ d\Omega$$

where W is the total center-of-mass energy. The intermediate states are simply specified by the direction of the center-of-mass momentum over which we sum.

Let us now consider forward elastic scattering. The initial and final states are identical, and (1-24) gives the imaginary part of M_{ii} as

$$2 \,\mathrm{Im}\,\{M_{ii}\} = (2\pi)^4 \sum_n \delta(P_i - P_n) \, |M_{in}|^2$$

or

$$\mathrm{Im}\,\{F_{ii}\} = 2E_1 E_2 (2\pi)^4 \sum_n \delta(P_i - P_n) \, |M_{in}|^2$$

As easily seen from (1-8) the right-hand side is simply related to the total cross section. In terms of center-of-mass variables, we have

$$\mathrm{Im}\,\{F_{ii}\} = 2qW\sigma_{tot} \tag{1-25}$$

If we introduce the center-of-mass, forward scattering amplitude defined by (1-10) and (1-12), we have

$$\mathrm{Im}\, f(0,0) = \frac{q}{4\pi}\, \sigma_{tot} \tag{1-26}$$

This is the optical theorem or the Bohr-Peierls-Placzek relation.

2

PARTIAL-WAVE AMPLITUDES

2–1 CENTER-OF-MASS SCATTERING AMPLITUDES

We now discuss in more detail the conditions implied by Lorentz invariance for a two-body collision a + b → c + d, studied in the center-of-mass system. The center-of-mass system is defined as the reference system where the total momentum $\mathbf{p}_a + \mathbf{p}_b = \mathbf{p}_c + \mathbf{p}_d$ is equal to zero. Invariance under space rotation, space inversion, and time reversal reduces the number of independent dynamical parameters that are necessary to describe a scattering process. The center-of-mass variables used throughout are the total energy W and the scattering angles θ and φ (Fig. 2-1).

W and cos θ are easily expressed in terms of the s and t invariant variables

$$W = \sqrt{s}$$

$$\cos\theta = \frac{t + 2E_1E_3 - m_1^2 - m_3^2}{2pq} \tag{2-1}$$

$$E_{1,2} = (q^2 + m_{1,2}^2)^{1/2} \qquad E_{3,4} = (p^2 + m_{3,4}^2)^{1/2}$$

where

$$q = \frac{1}{2W}\lambda(W,m_1,m_2)$$

$$p = \frac{1}{2W}\lambda(W,m_3,m_4)$$

with

$$\lambda(x,y,z) = [(x+y+z)(x+y-z)(x-y+z)(x-y-z)]^{1/2}$$

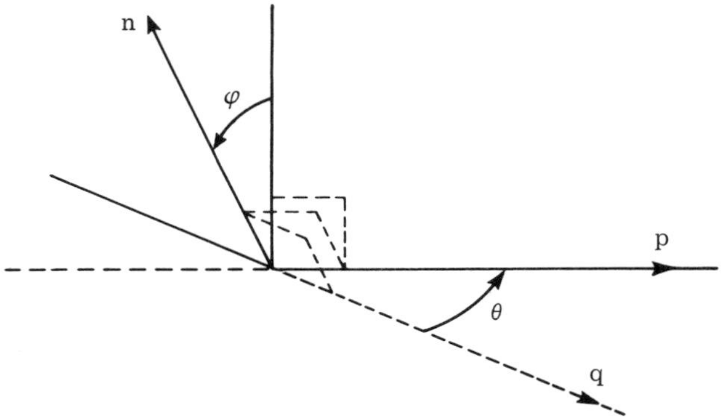

Figure 2-1

q and p are the center-of-mass momenta in the initial and final states.

The center-of-mass scattering amplitudes $f(W, \theta, \varphi)$ is normalized in such a way that the differential cross section reads

$$\frac{d\sigma}{d\Omega} = |f(W, \theta, \varphi)|^2 \tag{2-2}$$

This is quite generally the differential cross section for well-defined polarizations in the initial or final states.

For spinless particles $f(W, \theta, \varphi)$ is expanded into partial-wave amplitudes

$$f(W, \theta, \varphi) = \sum_{\ell} (2\ell + 1) f_{\ell}(W) P_{\ell}(\cos\theta) \tag{2-3}$$

with

$$f_{\ell}(W) = \tfrac{1}{2} \int_{-1}^{+1} f(W, \theta, \varphi) P_{\ell}(\cos\theta)\, d\cos\theta$$

Rotation invariance implies conservation of orbital angular momentum, and the scattering process can be separately considered for each partial wave at a time.

When the particles considered have spin, rotation invariance implies conservation of the total angular momentum j, and, for each value of j, there are several scattering amplitudes to consider and not just one as in (2-3). Let us then look back at the center-of-mass scattering amplitude for π-nucleon scattering

$$f_{fi} = \chi_f^{\dagger}(f_1 + f_2 \sigma\hat{p}_f \sigma\hat{p}_i)\chi_i \tag{1-17}$$

There is a priori a scattering amplitude attached to each of the two spin states of the nucleon in the initial as well as in the final states. If we consider helicity eigenstates (i.e., a $\pm\frac{1}{2}$ spin component along the center-of-mass momentum), χ_i (and χ_f) are eigenvectors of $\boldsymbol{\sigma}\hat{\mathbf{p}}_i$ (and $\boldsymbol{\sigma}\hat{\mathbf{p}}_f$); (1-17) already takes care of parity conservation.

We have two amplitudes to consider

$$\begin{aligned} F_{++} &= F_{--} = f_1 + f_2 \\ F_{+-} &= F_{-+} = f_1 - f_2 \end{aligned} \tag{2-4}$$

They are, respectively, the scattering amplitudes when the helicity of the nucleon does not change and when it changes. The subscripts on the amplitudes stand for the nucleon final and initial helicities. The helicity, defined as the component of the spin on the momentum, is defined, as well, to be the component of total angular momentum on the momentum. It is then invariant under rotation. The consideration of two helicity amplitudes (without change, and with change, of the nucleon helicity) will then be meaningful for each value of the total angular momentum. We can take care of the complications from the nucleon spin with two partial amplitudes f^j_{++} and f^j_{+-} for each j-value. We shall obtain them later as an illustration of the general formalism that we shall now develop for a two-body reaction with particles of arbitrary spin.

2–2 HELICITY FORMALISM

We now briefly present the most important relations obtained in the helicity formalism as applied to two-body reactions.[5] We first define center-of-mass, total, angular momentum eigenstates for two particles where each particle has a well-defined helicity denoted by λ. These states are written $|jm;\lambda_a\lambda_b\rangle$. $j(j+1)$ and m are the pertinent eigenvalues of $\mathbf{J}^2$ and J_z $(-j \le m \le j)$. The $2j+1$ vectors obtained for each j-value have to transform under rotation as basic vectors for the $2j+1$ dimensional, irreducible representation of the rotation group. They can easily be constructed in terms of plane wave states $|\theta,\varphi;\lambda_a\lambda_b\rangle$, where θ and φ define the direction of the relative momentum. The total momentum is zero.

Using the orthogonality properties for the coefficients of an irreducible unitary representation[6] we write

$$|jm;\lambda_a\lambda_b\rangle = \sqrt{\frac{2j+1}{4\pi}} \int \mathcal{D}^{j*}_{m\lambda}(\varphi,\theta,0)\, |\theta\varphi;\lambda_a\lambda_b\rangle\, d\Omega \tag{2-5}$$

$\lambda = \lambda_a - \lambda_b$. The integral is extended over the whole sphere

$d\Omega = \sin\theta\, d\theta\, d\varphi$. $\sqrt{(2j+1)/4\pi}$ is a normalization coefficient defined in such a way that

$$\langle j'\, m'; \lambda_1' \lambda_2' \mid jm; \lambda_1 \lambda_2 \rangle = \delta_{\lambda_1 \lambda_1'}\, \delta_{\lambda_2 \lambda_2'}\, \delta_{jj'}\, \delta_{mm'}$$

$\mathfrak{D}^j(\alpha,\beta,\gamma)$ are the well-known rotation matrices[6]

$$R_{\alpha\beta\gamma} \mid j,m\rangle = \sum_{m'} \mathfrak{D}^j_{m'm}(\alpha,\beta,\gamma) \mid j,m'\rangle$$

where $R_{\alpha\beta\gamma}$ stands for the rotation operator with Euler angles α, β, γ. The angular dependence of the wave function is given by a $\mathfrak{D}$-function instead of a spherical harmonic function which comes in for spinless particles. It reads

$$\langle \theta\varphi; \lambda_1 \lambda_2 \mid jm; \lambda_1 \lambda_2 \rangle = \sqrt{\frac{2j+1}{4\pi}}\; \mathfrak{D}^{j*}_{m\lambda}(\varphi,\theta,0) \tag{2-6}$$

Note the absence of Clebsch-Gordan coefficients.

A T-matrix element is written as follows:

$$T_{fi} = (2\pi)^4\, \delta(p_i - p_f) R \langle \theta_f\, \varphi_f \mid T \mid \theta_i\, \varphi_i \rangle \tag{2-7}$$

Since we have conservation of total energy and momentum we just need the c.m. relative momentum direction θ,φ to specify a state. Free-particle states have already been normalized according to (1-4): $\langle \mathbf{p}_1', \mathbf{p}_2' \mid \mathbf{p}_1, \mathbf{p}_2 \rangle = (2\pi)^6\, \delta(\mathbf{p}_1 - \mathbf{p}_1')\, \delta(\mathbf{p}_2 - \mathbf{p}_2')$. To keep this together with a convenient center-of-mass normalization $\langle \theta'\varphi' \mid \theta\varphi \rangle = \delta(\varphi - \varphi')\, \delta(\cos\theta - \cos\theta')$, a kinematical factor R has to be introduced. Taking the unit matrix as a particular case in (2-7) one easily obtains

$$R = (2\pi)^2 \frac{W}{\sqrt{qpE_1 E_2 E_3 E_4}}$$

With (2-6) and (1-6) we get

$$F_{fi} = (2\pi)^2 \frac{W}{\sqrt{pq}} \langle \theta_f\, \varphi_f \mid T \mid \theta_i\, \varphi_i \rangle$$

which together with (1-9) gives for the center-of-mass differential cross section

$$\frac{d\sigma}{d\Omega} = \left(\frac{2\pi}{q}\right)^2 \mid \langle \theta_f\, \varphi_f \mid T \mid \theta_i\, \varphi_i \rangle \mid^2 \tag{2-8}$$

Now write

$$\langle \theta_f \varphi_f \mid T \mid \theta_i \varphi_i \rangle$$
$$= \sum_{jm} \sum_{j'm'} \langle \theta_f \varphi_f \mid j'm' \rangle \langle j'm' \mid T \mid jm \rangle \langle jm \mid \theta_i \varphi_i \rangle$$

Rotation invariance takes on the simple form

$$\langle j'm' \mid T \mid jm \rangle = \delta_{jj'} \, \delta_{mm'} \, T^j(W) \tag{2-9}$$

Taking the z-axis along the initial momentum $(\theta_i, \varphi_i) = (0,0)$ and using (2-6) we write (2-8) as

$$\frac{d\sigma}{d\Omega} = \mid f_{\lambda_3\lambda_4\lambda_1\lambda_2}(\theta,\varphi) \mid^2 \tag{2-10}$$

with the helicity amplitudes defined as

$$f_{\lambda_3\lambda_4\lambda_1\lambda_2}(\theta,\varphi) = \frac{1}{q} \sum_j (j + \tfrac{1}{2}) \langle \lambda_3\lambda_4 \mid T^j(W) \mid \lambda_1\lambda_2 \rangle$$
$$\times \mathfrak{D}^{j*}_{\lambda\mu}(\varphi,\theta,0) \tag{2-11}$$

λ_1, λ_2 (λ_3, λ_4) are the helicities of the initial and final particles. Their spins will be denoted by S_1, S_2 (S_3, S_4). This relation generalizes (2-3) for arbitrary spins. The $\mathfrak{D}$-functions replace the Legendre polynomials. Note the absence of Clebsch-Gordan coefficients. The formula is relativistically correct and applies equally well for massless particles.

2–3 INVARIANCE UNDER PARITY AND TIME REVERSAL

With (2-10) and (2-11) we need a priori $(2S_3 + 1)(2S_4 + 1)(2S_1 + 1) \times (2S_2 + 1)$ amplitudes for each j-value. Invariance under parity, and time reversal, reduces a great deal the number of independent ones. The helicity, defined as $\mathbf{J} \cdot \mathbf{P}/\mid \mathbf{P} \mid$, where $\mathbf{J}$ is the angular momentum and $\mathbf{P}$ the momentum, is not invariant under space inversion. $\mathbf{J}$ does not change but $\mathbf{P}$ does change sign. Hence a state with helicity λ is transformed into a state with helicity $-\lambda$. One shows that[5]

$$P \mid jm; \lambda_1, \lambda_2 \rangle = \eta_1 \eta_2 (-1)^{j - S_1 - S_2} \mid jm; -\lambda_1, -\lambda_2 \rangle \tag{2-12}$$

where η_1 and η_2 are the intrinsic parities of the two particles of spin S_1 and S_2. P stands for the parity operator.

Invariance of the S-matrix under parity implies that $PSP^{-1} = S$.

With (2-11) and (2-12) this gives a relation between matrix elements with states of opposite helicities. Namely:

$$\langle -\lambda_3, -\lambda_4 \mid T^j(W) \mid -\lambda_1, -\lambda_2 \rangle$$

$$= \frac{\eta_3 \eta_4}{\eta_1 \eta_2} (-1)^{S_3+S_4-S_1-S_2} \langle \lambda_3 \lambda_4 \mid T^j(W) \mid \lambda_1 \lambda_2 \rangle \qquad (2\text{-}13)$$

Under time reversal both **J** and **P** change sign; the helicity does not change. By applying time reversal, T, to the state (2-5), we find a new state with the same angular momentum and helicities but with an opposite eigenvalue for J_z. With the phase convention given in Ref. 5 one gets

$$T \mid jm; \lambda_1, \lambda_2 \rangle = (-1)^{j-m} \mid j - m; \lambda_1, \lambda_2 \rangle \qquad (2\text{-}14)$$

Invariance under time reversal implies $TST^{-1} = S^\dagger$. Together with (2-11) and (2-14) this gives the familiar relation between T-matrix elements

$$\langle \lambda_3 \lambda_4 \mid T^j(W) \mid \lambda_1 \lambda_2 \rangle = \langle \lambda_1 \lambda_2 \mid T^j(W) \mid \lambda_3 \lambda_4 \rangle \qquad (2\text{-}15)$$

Let us consider elastic scattering and write the $((2S_1 + 1)(2S_2 + 1))^2$ helicity amplitudes for each value of j in a matrix form, the initial states (columns) and the final states (rows) having the same ordering. For small j-values the number of rows and columns may be artificially reduced since obviously $\lambda \leq j$ and $\mu \leq j$. Relation (2-13) implies a symmetry (up to a common sign) with respect to the center. Relation (2-15) implies a symmetry with respect to the principal diagonal. This gives the number of independent amplitudes. For identical particle scattering one finds a further relation

$$\langle \lambda_3 \lambda_4 \mid T^j(W) \mid \lambda_1 \lambda_2 \rangle = \langle \lambda_4 \lambda_3 \mid T^j(W) \mid \lambda_2 \lambda_1 \rangle \qquad (2\text{-}16)$$

In (2-11) each matrix element is multiplied by a $\mathfrak{D}$-function. The symmetry relations found for the matrix elements correspond to changing the signs of both λ and μ (parity) or to the exchange of λ and μ (time reversal). Now

$$\mathfrak{D}^{j*}_{\lambda\mu}(\varphi, \theta, 0) = e^{i\lambda\varphi} \, d^j_{\lambda\mu}(\theta)$$

with

$$d^j_{\lambda\mu}(\theta) = (-1)^{\lambda-\mu} \, d^j_{-\lambda-\mu}(\theta) = (-1)^{\lambda-\mu} \, d^j_{\mu\lambda}(\theta)$$

	+ +	+ −	− +	− −
+ +	f_1^j	f_5^j	f_5^j	f_2^j
+ −	f_5^j	f_3^j	f_4^j	f_5^j
− +	f_5^j	f_4^j	f_3^j	f_5^j
− −	f_2^j	f_5^j	f_5^j	f_1^j

(a)

	+ +	+ −	− +	− −
+ +	f_1	f_5	$-f_5$	f_2
+ −	$-f_5$	f_3	f_4	$-f_5$
− +	f_5	f_4	f_3	f_5
− −	f_2	f_5	$-f_5$	f_1

(b)

Figure 2-2
Relations among partial amplitude and scattering amplitude at $\varphi = 0$, obtained for proton-proton scattering.

These relations are independent of j, and the relations found among the partial scattering amplitudes give the same relations up to a sign and the trivial φ-dependence among the full scattering amplitudes (2-11). Since the number of independent amplitudes is obviously equal to the number of independent invariant functions, we have a simple procedure to get this number. For proton-proton scattering (Fig. 2-2) we obtain 5 independent amplitudes. Using (2-13), we reduce this number of amplitudes from 16 to 8. Then, by employing (2-15) we go from 8 to 6 and finally with (2-16), from 6 to 5. For π-nucleon scattering, with (2-13) we reduce from 4, which has to be considered a priori, to 2. (2-15) gives nothing else.

2–4 PION-NUCLEON SCATTERING AMPLITUDES

Invariance under parity implies

$$\langle \tfrac{1}{2} \mid T^j(W) \mid \tfrac{1}{2} \rangle = \langle -\tfrac{1}{2} \mid T^j(W) \mid -\tfrac{1}{2} \rangle$$

and

$$\langle \tfrac{1}{2} \mid T^j(W) \mid -\tfrac{1}{2} \rangle = \langle -\tfrac{1}{2} \mid T^j(W) \mid \tfrac{1}{2} \rangle$$

Introduce two partial amplitudes:

$$f^j_{++} = \frac{\langle \tfrac{1}{2} \mid T^j \mid \tfrac{1}{2} \rangle}{2q} \qquad f^j_{-+} = \frac{\langle -\tfrac{1}{2} \mid T^j \mid \tfrac{1}{2} \rangle}{2q}$$

(2-11) gives the two helicity amplitudes

$$
\begin{aligned}
f_{++}(\theta,\varphi) &= \sum_j (2j+1) f^j_{++} \mathfrak{D}^{j*}_{1/2\ 1/2}(\varphi,\theta,0) \\
f_{-+}(\theta,\varphi) &= \sum_j (2j+1) f^j_{-+} \mathfrak{D}^{j*}_{(1/2)\,-(1/2)}(\varphi,\theta,0)
\end{aligned}
\tag{2-17}
$$

From the orthogonality property of the $\mathfrak{D}$-functions we express $f^j_{\lambda\mu}$ in terms of $f_{\lambda\mu}$.

$$
\begin{aligned}
f^j_{++} &= \frac{1}{4\pi} \int f_{++}(\theta,\varphi) \mathfrak{D}^j_{1/2\ 1/2}(\varphi,\theta,0)\ d\Omega \\
f^j_{++} &= \frac{1}{4\pi} \int f_{++}(\theta,\varphi) \\
&\quad \frac{e^{-i\varphi/2}\left(P'_{j+(1/2)}(\cos\theta) - P'_{j-(1/2)}(\cos\theta)\right)\cos\theta/2\ d\Omega}{j+\frac{1}{2}}
\end{aligned}
\tag{2-18}
$$

and

$$
f^j_{-+} = \frac{1}{4\pi} \int f_{-+}(\theta,\varphi) \mathfrak{D}^j_{(1/2)-(1/2)}(\varphi,\theta,0)\ d\Omega
$$

$$
\begin{aligned}
f^j_{-+} &= -\frac{1}{4\pi} \int f_{-+}(\theta,\varphi) \\
&\times \frac{e^{-i\varphi/2}\sin\theta/2\left(P'_{j+(1/2)}(\cos\theta) + P'_{j-(1/2)}(\cos\theta)\right) d\Omega}{j+\frac{1}{2}}
\end{aligned}
$$

the $\mathfrak{D}$-function being expressed in terms of first derivative of Legendre polynomials.

To compute the helicity amplitudes f_{++} and f_{-+} from f_1 and f_2 we take $\chi_i = \chi_+$ and we have to take for χ_f the two helicity states

$$
\cos\frac{\theta}{2}\ e^{-i\varphi/2}\ \chi_+ + \sin\frac{\theta}{2}\ e^{i\varphi/2}\ \chi_-
$$

and

$$
-\sin\frac{\theta}{2}\ e^{-i\varphi/2}\ \chi_+ + \cos\frac{\theta}{2}\ e^{i\varphi/2}\ \chi_-
$$

χ_- being a negative helicity state for the initial nucleon. This gives

$$f_{++}(\theta,\varphi) = \cos\frac{\theta}{2}\, e^{i\varphi/2}\,(f_1 + f_2)$$

$$f_{-+}(\theta,\varphi) = \sin\frac{\theta}{2}\, e^{i\varphi/2}\,(f_1 - f_2) \tag{2-19}$$

Now combine (2-18) and (2-19) and use the well-known properties of the Legendre polynomials. This gives

$$f^j_{++} = \tfrac{1}{4}\int_{-1}^{+1} (f_1 + f_2)\left(P_{j+(1/2)}(x) - P_{j-(1/2)}(x)\right) dx$$

$$f^j_{-+} = \tfrac{1}{4}\int_{-1}^{+1} (f_1 - f_2)\left(P_{j-(1/2)}(x) - P_{j+(1/2)}(x)\right) dx \tag{2-20}$$

and, conversely,

$$f_1 = \sum_j \left\{ f^j_{++}\left(P'_{j+(1/2)}(x) - P'_{j-(1/2)}(x)\right) + f^j_{-+}\left(P'_{j+(1/2)}(x) + P'_{j-(1/2)}(x)\right)\right\}$$

$$f_2 = \sum_j \left\{ f^j_{++}\left(P'_{j+(1/2)}(x) - P'_{j-(1/2)}(x)\right) - f^j_{-+}\left(P'_{j+(1/2)}(x) + P'_{j-(1/2)}(x)\right)\right\}$$

This is what comes out in the helicity formalism, and the algebra can easily be generalized to any two-body process. In π-nucleon scattering, though, there is the important fact that the two independent amplitudes found for each j-value can be defined according to the parity of the states.

For each value of the total angular momentum there are two values of the orbital angular momentum $j \pm \frac{1}{2}$ which are denoted by $(\ell + 1)_-$ and ℓ_+. The subscript refers to the fact that j is equal either to $(\ell_+ + \frac{1}{2})$ or $((\ell + 1)_- - \frac{1}{2})$. The parity of an orbital, angular momentum eigenstate is $-(-1)^\ell$. For the states defined by j, ℓ_+ and $j, (\ell + 1)_-$, we have, respectively, parity $\pm(-1)^{j+(1/2)}$. With parity conservation such states do not mix in scattering as helicity eigenstates do, and unitarity takes a very simple form as long as scattering is purely elastic. Each submatrix S^j reads $e^{2i\,\delta_{\ell\pm}}$, where $\delta_{\ell_\pm}$ is the phase shift (a real quantity).

Two scattering amplitudes are considered for each j-value, namely,

$$f_{\ell j} = \frac{T_{\ell j}}{2q} = \frac{e^{i\delta_{\ell j}} \sin \delta_{\ell j}}{q} \tag{2-21}$$

It is an easy matter to go from the partial helicity amplitudes, previously defined, to these partial-wave amplitudes. We have to write parity eigenstates in terms of helicity states. From (2-12) we see that the states

$$\frac{1}{\sqrt{2}} (|\, jm, \lambda\rangle \pm |\, jm, -\lambda\rangle)$$

are eigenstates of the parity operator with eigenvalues $\pm(-1)^{j+(1/2)}$. The scattering amplitude for the first one (upper sign) is $f_{\ell+}$, for the second one, it is $f_{(\ell+1)_-}$. Hence

$$\begin{aligned} f_{\ell+} &= f^j_{++} + f^j_{-+} \\ f_{(\ell+1)_-} &= f^j_{++} - f^j_{-+} \end{aligned} \tag{2-22}$$

From (2-22) and (2-20) we then obtain the usual partial-wave expansions

$$f_{\ell\pm} = \tfrac{1}{2} \int_{-1}^{+1} (f_1 P_\ell(x) + f_2 P_{\ell\pm 1}(x))\, dx \tag{2-23}$$

and, conversely,

$$\begin{aligned} f_1 &= \sum_\ell \left(f_{\ell+} P'_{\ell+1}(x) - f_{\ell-} P'_{\ell-1}(x)\right) \\ f_2 &= \sum_\ell \left(f_{\ell-} - f_{\ell+}\right) P'_\ell(x) \end{aligned} \tag{2-24}$$

Writing $f_1 + f_2\, \sigma \hat{q}_2 \sigma \hat{q}_1$ as $f_1 + f_2 x + i f_2\, \sigma \hat{q}_2 x \hat{q}_1$, one defines the spin-flip f_2 and the non-spin-flip amplitude $F_1 = f_1 + f_2 x$, which reads

$$F_1 = \sum_\ell \left((\ell + 1) f_{\ell+} + \ell f_{\ell-}\right) P_\ell(x)$$

2–5 DIFFERENTIAL CROSS SECTION AND POLARIZATION

We now go back to the general case of two-body scattering. The center-of-mass differential cross section is easily obtained in the helicity formalism. This follows from the simple orthogonality relation of the helicity states. From (2-11) we have

$$\frac{d\sigma}{d\Omega} = \rho_{\lambda_1\lambda_2} \sum_{jj'} (2j+1)(2j'+1) f^{j}_{\lambda'\lambda} f^{j'*}_{\lambda'\lambda}$$

$$\times\, \mathfrak{D}^{j*}_{\lambda'\lambda}(\varphi,\theta,0)\,\mathfrak{D}^{j'}_{\lambda'\lambda}(\varphi,\theta,0)$$

with

$$f^{j}_{\lambda'\lambda} = \frac{\langle\lambda_3\lambda_4 \mid T^j(W) \mid \lambda_1\lambda_2\rangle}{2q}$$

ρ is the density matrix that describes the initial state. We further write, introducing Clebsch-Gordan coefficients,[7]

$$\mathfrak{D}^{j*}_{\lambda'\lambda}(\varphi,\theta,0)\,\mathfrak{D}^{j'}_{\lambda'\lambda}(\varphi,\theta,0)$$

$$= \sum_{\ell} (-1)^{\lambda-\lambda'}\, C(jj'\ell \mid \lambda,-\lambda)\, C(jj'\ell \mid \lambda',-\lambda')\, P_\ell(\cos\theta)$$

so that the differential cross section is expressed in terms of Legendre polynomials. If the initial beam or target is not polarized and if the polarization of the final particles are not observed, we sum over λ_3 and λ_4 and use symmetry properties of the Clebsch-Gordan coefficients to obtain

$$\frac{d\sigma}{d\Omega} = \frac{1}{(2S_1+1)(2S_2+1)} \sum_{(\lambda)} \sum_{jj'} (2j+1)(2j'+1)\ \mathrm{Re}\left\{f^{j}_{\lambda'\lambda} f^{j'*}_{\lambda'\lambda}\right\}$$

$$\times \sum_{\ell} (-1)^{\lambda-\lambda'}\, C(jj'\ell \mid \lambda,-\lambda)$$

$$\times\, C(jj'\ell \mid \lambda',-\lambda')\, P_\ell(\cos\theta) \qquad (2\text{-}25)$$

where $\Sigma_{(\lambda)}$ stands for a summation over all possible helicities, and Re stands for real part of the bracket.

Since the polarization of the two particles is considered separately, formulas giving polarizations take a simple form. As an example, let us consider the transverse polarization of one final particle when the initial particles are not polarized and when the polarization of the other final particle is not observed. The polarization (of particle 3 of spin S_3) normal to the production plane reads (Fig. 2-1)

$$\langle \mathbf{S}\cdot\hat{n}\rangle \frac{d\sigma}{d\Omega} = \frac{1}{(2S_1+1)(2S_2+1)} \sum_{(\lambda)} \sqrt{(S_3+\lambda_3)(S_3-\lambda_3+1)}$$

$$\times\ \mathrm{Im}\left\{ f_{\lambda_{3-1}\lambda_4\lambda_1\lambda_2}\, f^{*}_{\lambda_3\lambda_4\lambda_1\lambda_2} \right\}$$

$\hat{n}$ is a unit vector normal to the production plane. Together with (2-11) this gives

$$\langle \mathbf{S}\cdot\hat{n}\rangle \frac{d\sigma}{d\Omega} = \frac{\sqrt{2S_3(S_3+1)}}{(2S_1+1)(2S_2+1)} \sum_{(\lambda)} \sum_{jj'} (2j+1)(2j'+1)$$

$$\times\ \mathrm{Im}\left\{ f^{j}_{\lambda_3\lambda_4\lambda_1\lambda_2}\, f^{j'*}_{\lambda_{3-1}\lambda_4\lambda_1\lambda_2} \right\}$$

$$\times \sum_{\ell} (-1)^{\lambda-\lambda'}\ C(jj'\ell \mid \lambda_1 - \lambda)\, C(jj'\ell \mid \mu, 1-\mu)$$

$$\times\ C(S_3\,1\,S_3 \mid \lambda_3, -1)\ \frac{\sin\theta\, P'_\ell \cos\theta}{\sqrt{\ell(\ell+1)}} \qquad (2\text{-}26)$$

Im stands for the imaginary part of the bracket. By taking the simple case of π-nucleon scattering, we obtain the recoil nucleon, transverse polarization for nonpolarized beam and target in terms of f_1 and f_2 from (2-19). It reads

$$\langle \mathbf{S}\cdot\hat{n}\rangle \frac{d\sigma}{d\Omega} = \sin\theta\ \mathrm{Im}\,\{f_2 f_1^*\} \qquad (2\text{-}27)$$

Now expand f_1 and f_2 according to (2-24) and assume that there are only even (or odd) partial waves. f_1 will only have first derivative of odd (or even) Legendre polynomials, and f_2 will only have first derivative of even (or odd) Legendre polynomials. Hence the product is odd with respect to the exchange of $\cos\theta$ into $-\cos\theta$ and the transverse polarization vanishes at right angle in the center-of-mass system. Conversely, the observation of such a polarization for the recoil nucleon from a nonpolarized initial state implies interference between partial waves of opposite parities. This result can be extended to pion photoproduction.

2–6 UNITARITY RELATION FOR PARTIAL-WAVE AMPLITUDES

Unitarity implies that each submatrix $S^j(W)$ which corresponds to a given eigenvalue of total angular momentum is a unitary operator. For spinless-particle elastic scattering, or for a spin-0 and spin-$\frac{1}{2}$ particle scattering (when parity is conserved) this is very simply expressed. Each S^j-matrix reduces to a phase factor $e^{2i\,\delta_{\ell j}}$, where $\delta_{\ell j}$ is the phase shift (a real quantity). The scattering amplitude is written as (2-21),

$$f_{\ell j} = \frac{e^{i\,\delta_{\ell j}} \sin \delta_{\ell j}}{q}$$

When both particles have spin, or when inelastic scattering also occurs, this is no longer true. Nevertheless we can write the unitarity relation (1-23) for each particular T^j-matrix. It reads

$$-i\left(T^j_{fi} - T^{j*}_{if}\right) = \sum_n T^j_{fn}\, T^{j*}_{in}$$

With the phase convention taken, time reversal invariance gives (2-16)

$$2 \operatorname{Im} T^j_{fi} = \sum_n T^j_{fn}\, T^{j*}_{ni} \tag{2-28}$$

It often happens that, among all the intermediate states that are included in (2-28), only one gives an important contribution. Let us assume for instance that it is, in fact, identical to the final state. We write

$$2 \operatorname{Im} T^j_{fi} \simeq T^j_{ff}\, T^{j*}_{fi}$$

The assumption made, implies that the first matrix element on the right-hand side refers to elastic scattering, when inelastic processes are negligible.

Therefore

$$T^j_{ff} \simeq 2e^{i\,\delta_j} \sin \delta_j$$

where δ_j is a real number and

$$\text{Im}\ T_{fi}^{j} \simeq e^{i\,\delta_j} \sin\delta_j\ T_{fi}^{j*}$$

The phase of the transition matrix element is then equal to the scattering phase shift in final state.

Such an approximation is legitimate for pion photoproduction. Whenever there is a π-nucleon resonance, i.e., a rapid variation with energy of the scattering phase shift, this will also affect photoproduction.

It is easy to check that the optical theorem holds for each partial wave or helicity amplitude. Namely,

$$(2j+1)\ \text{Im}\ f_{\lambda\lambda}^{j} = \frac{q}{4\pi}\sigma_{tot}^{j,\lambda} \tag{2-29}$$

3

CHARGE INDEPENDENCE

3–1 CHARGE SYMMETRY AND CHARGE INDEPENDENCE

To analyze collisions between charged particles such as π-mesons and nucleons, there are a priori as many amplitudes to consider as possible charge configurations in the initial and final states, which are allowed by the conservation of charge. The number of independent amplitudes is, however, much lower, as follows from the charge-independence property of strong interactions.

Studies of nuclear levels in light nuclei and of low-energy nucleon-nucleon scattering showed two important features of nuclear interactions. First nuclear forces between two protons or two neutrons in the same quantum state are the same. This is charge symmetry; and, second, nuclear forces between two nucleons (proton or neutron) in the same quantum state are the same. This is charge independence of nuclear forces, which of course includes charge symmetry. The statements are not exactly correct since Coulomb interactions differ according to charge configurations. However, deviations from what is expected from charge independence may always be explained in terms of small and often calculable Coulomb corrections.

As nuclear forces have mainly their origin in the exchange of π-mesons, charge symmetry and charge independence were further tested in and applied to π-nucleon interactions and later extended to all strongly interacting particles.

In fact, these particles always appear as members of charge multiplets of particles, with almost identical properties and masses (proton or neutron, π^+, π^0, π^-, Σ^+, Σ^0, Σ^-, . . .). The small mass differences found among the members of each multiplet is of the order of what one should expect from Coulomb corrections. One then gathers the members of each multiplet under a single name (nucleon, pion, sigma, ...) referring to one particle only, produced in different charge states.

These charge states are considered as basic vectors in charge space. It is a natural idea to associate charge independence with a particular invariance property under transformations in charge space. In order to obtain unitary transformations in charge space, the rotation group in three dimensions proved to be extremely useful to consider. The members of each multiplet are then considered as a basic for an irreducible representation. They all have in common one quantum number which, in analogy with spin, is called "isotopic spin." The nucleon and pion, and sigma are, respectively, isotopic spin doublet and triplet with isotopic spin $\frac{1}{2}$ ($\mathbf{T}^2 = \frac{3}{4}$) and $1(\mathbf{T}^2 = 2)$. The Λ^0 is an isotopic spin singlet.

The three components of the isotopic spin operator obey the commutation rules for angular momentum

$$\begin{aligned} [T_i, T_j] &= i\epsilon_{ijk} T_k \\ [\mathbf{T}^2, T_i] &= 0 \end{aligned} \tag{3-1}$$

The rotation operator for a rotation of angle φ around an axis $\mathbf{n}$ reads $R_\varphi = \exp(-i\varphi\mathbf{T}\cdot\hat{n})$, where $\hat{n}$ is a unit vector along $\mathbf{n}$.

Charge states in each multiplet correspond to the $2T + 1$ eigenstates of T_3. As is well known for angular momentum, the operators $T_+ = T_1 + iT_2$ (and $T_- = T_1 - iT_2$) increases (and decreases) the charge by one unit. The isotopic spin quantum number proved to be a fundamental label to be associated to each strongly interacting particle. It is not, however, a directly measurable quantity such as charge or angular momentum. In this respect, it is similar to the baryonic quantum number N, and the strangeness quantum number S. The charge Q is related to T_3 through

$$Q = T_3 + \frac{N + S}{2} \tag{3-2}$$

Conservation of charge baryonic number and strangeness implies conservation of T_3.

With several particles, isotopic spin adds as angular momentum. A total isotopic spin is defined.

Charge independence is expressed as rotation invariance in charge space. If it holds, total isotopic spin is conserved, together with T_3, in strong interactions, and there is one single amplitude to consider for each value of the total isotopic spin. These are the independent amplitudes. Each particular charge amplitude is then easily obtained with the Clebsch-Gordan coefficients used to construct total isotopic spin eigenstates in terms of the individual particle charge states. This will be illustrated in detail for π-nucleon scattering.

3–2 ISOTOPIC SPIN FORMALISM FOR PIONS AND NUCLEONS

The three orthogonal charge states of the π-meson $|\pi^+\rangle$, $|\pi^-\rangle$, and $|\pi^0\rangle$ form a basis for an irreducible representation of dimension 3 of the rotation group in three dimensions. By taking T_3 diagonal, we have a 3×3 matrix representation

$$t_3 = \begin{pmatrix} 1 & 0 & 0 \\ 0 & 0 & 0 \\ 0 & 0 & -1 \end{pmatrix} \qquad t_1 = \frac{1}{\sqrt{2}} \begin{pmatrix} 0 & -1 & 0 \\ -1 & 0 & 1 \\ 0 & 1 & 0 \end{pmatrix} \qquad t_2 = \frac{i}{\sqrt{2}} \begin{pmatrix} 0 & 1 & 0 \\ -1 & 0 & -1 \\ 0 & 1 & 0 \end{pmatrix}$$

with

$$\mathbf{t}^2 = 2 \begin{pmatrix} 1 & 0 & 0 \\ 0 & 1 & 0 \\ 0 & 0 & 1 \end{pmatrix} \tag{3-3}$$

Besides these three charge states, it is useful to consider another basis defined as follows:

$$\begin{aligned} |\pi_1\rangle &= \frac{1}{\sqrt{2}} (|\pi^+\rangle + |\pi^-\rangle) \\ |\pi_2\rangle &= -\frac{i}{\sqrt{2}} (|\pi^+\rangle - |\pi^-\rangle) \\ |\pi_3\rangle &= |\pi^0\rangle \end{aligned} \tag{3-4}$$

Under rotation in charge space, $|\pi_1\rangle$, $|\pi_2\rangle$, and $|\pi_3\rangle$ now behave like the cartesian components of a vector. The matrix elements of T_i $(i = 1,2,3)$ between any two of these new states is quite simple. It reads

$$\langle \pi_j | T_i | \pi_k \rangle = -i\epsilon_{ijk} \tag{3-5}$$

In field theory the isotopic spin operator for the pion system is expressed in terms of the pion fields as[8]

$$\mathbf{T} = -\int :(\pi(x) \times \phi(x)): \; d^3x \tag{3-6}$$

φ_1, ϕ_2, and φ_3 are the hermitian field operators describing the pion system; π_1, π_2, and π_3 their conjugate momenta. It is easy to check that (3-6) satisfies (3-1) and that the ϕ_i fields transform like the cartesian components of a vector under rotation in charge space.

For a 2π-meson system, total isotopic spin is equal to either 0, 1, or 2. Eigenstates of the total isotopic spin operator $\mathbf{t}(1) + \mathbf{t}(2)$ can be constructed in terms of individual pion charge states. This is shown in Table 3-1.

The two charge states of the nucleon-proton $|p\rangle$ and neutron $|n\rangle$—form a basis for a representation of dimension 2. The 2×2 matrix representation of isotopic spin is given by the Pauli matrices $\boldsymbol{\tau}/2$. $|p\rangle$ and $|n\rangle$ are eigenstates of τ_3 with eigenvalues +1 and −1.

In field theory the isotopic spin operator for the nucleon system is defined by the Wick product[8]

$$\mathbf{T} = \tfrac{1}{2} : \int \psi_N^\dagger(x)\, \boldsymbol{\tau}\, \psi_N(x) \; d^3x : \tag{3-7}$$

where ψ_N is the nucleon field (four proton and four neutron components).

If I stands for the 4×4 unit matrix,

$$\tau_1 = \begin{pmatrix} 0 & I \\ I & 0 \end{pmatrix} \qquad \tau_2 = i\begin{pmatrix} 0 & -I \\ I & 0 \end{pmatrix} \qquad \tau_3 = \begin{pmatrix} 1 & 0 \\ 0 & -1 \end{pmatrix}$$

For a two-nucleon system we have total isotopic spin 0 and 1. It is easy to see that

$$\Lambda_1 = \frac{3 + \boldsymbol{\tau}(1)\cdot\boldsymbol{\tau}(2)}{4} \qquad \text{and} \qquad \Lambda_0 = \frac{1 - \boldsymbol{\tau}(1)\cdot\boldsymbol{\tau}(2)}{4} \tag{3-8}$$

are, respectively, projection operators on the T = 1 and T = 0 states.

Table 3-1

T_3	T = 2	T = 1	T = 0
2	$\lvert\pi_1^+\pi_2^+\rangle$		
1	$\dfrac{\lvert\pi_1^0\pi_2^+\rangle + \lvert\pi_1^+\pi_2^0\rangle}{\sqrt{2}}$	$\dfrac{\lvert\pi_1^+\pi_2^0\rangle - \lvert\pi_1^0\pi_2^+\rangle}{\sqrt{2}}$	
0	$\dfrac{\lvert\pi_1^-\pi_2^+\rangle + 2\lvert\pi_1^0\pi_2^0\rangle + \lvert\pi_1^+\pi_2^-\rangle}{\sqrt{6}}$	$\dfrac{\lvert\pi_1^+\pi_2^-\rangle - \lvert\pi_1^-\pi_2^+\rangle}{\sqrt{2}}$	$\dfrac{\lvert\pi_1^-\pi_2^+\rangle - \lvert\pi_1^0\pi_2^0\rangle + \lvert\pi_1^+\pi_2^-\rangle}{\sqrt{3}}$
−1	$\dfrac{\lvert\pi_1^0\pi_2^-\rangle + \lvert\pi_1^-\pi_2^0\rangle}{\sqrt{2}}$	$\dfrac{\lvert\pi_1^0\pi_2^-\rangle - \lvert\pi_1^-\pi_2^0\rangle}{\sqrt{2}}$	
−2	$\lvert\pi_1^-\pi_2^-\rangle$		

Table 3-2

T_3	$T = 1$	$T = 0$
+1	$\lvert p_1 p_2 \rangle$	
0	$\frac{1}{\sqrt{2}}(\lvert p_1 n_2\rangle + \lvert n_1 p_2\rangle)$	$\frac{1}{\sqrt{2}}(\lvert p_1 n_2\rangle - \lvert n_1 p_2\rangle)$
−1	$\lvert n_1 n_2 \rangle$	

In terms of individual nucleon states we construct eigenstates of the total isotopic spin $\frac{1}{2}[\boldsymbol{\tau}(1) + \boldsymbol{\tau}(2)]$ (Table 3-2).

3–3 ISOTOPIC SPIN FORMALISM IN PION-NUCLEON SCATTERING

In π-nucleon scattering we have six charge states

$$\lvert p\pi^+\rangle,\ \lvert p\pi^-\rangle,\ \lvert p\pi^0\rangle \qquad \text{and} \qquad \lvert n\pi^-\rangle,\ \lvert n\pi^+\rangle,\ \lvert n\pi^0\rangle$$

In order to exhibit conveniently charge independence we introduce the more convenient charge states that are eigenstates of total isotopic spin: $\mathbf{T}^2$ and T_3. To this end, we couple isotopic spin $\frac{1}{2}$ and isotopic spin 1 to obtain total isotopic spin $\frac{3}{2}$ or $\frac{1}{2}$. All six charge amplitudes are then expressed in terms of the scattering amplitudes with isotopic spin $\frac{3}{2}$ and $\frac{1}{2}$ ($F^{3/2}$ and $F^{1/2}$) (Table 3-3), and conversely:

$$\begin{aligned}
\lvert p\pi^0\rangle &= \frac{1}{\sqrt{3}}(\lvert \tfrac{1}{2}, \tfrac{1}{2}\rangle - \sqrt{2}\,\lvert \tfrac{3}{2}, \tfrac{1}{2}\rangle) \\
\lvert p\pi^-\rangle &= \frac{1}{\sqrt{3}}(\sqrt{2}\,\lvert \tfrac{1}{2}, -\tfrac{1}{2}\rangle + \lvert \tfrac{3}{2}, -\tfrac{1}{2}\rangle) \\
\lvert n\pi^+\rangle &= \frac{1}{\sqrt{3}}(\lvert \tfrac{3}{2}, \tfrac{1}{2}\rangle + \sqrt{2}\,\lvert \tfrac{1}{2}, \tfrac{1}{2}\rangle) \\
\lvert n\pi^0\rangle &= \frac{1}{\sqrt{3}}(\sqrt{2}\,\lvert \tfrac{3}{2}, -\tfrac{1}{2}\rangle - \lvert \tfrac{1}{2}, -\tfrac{1}{2}\rangle)
\end{aligned} \tag{3-9}$$

For pure elastic scattering it follows that

$F_{\pi^+p} = F^{3/2}$ $\qquad$ $\pi^+p \to \pi^+p$ or $\pi^-n \to \pi^-n$ (charge symmetry)

$F_{\pi^-p} = \frac{1}{3}(F^{3/2} + 2F^{1/2})$ $\qquad$ $\pi^-p \to \pi^-p$ or $\pi^+n \to \pi^+n$

Table 3-3

T_3	$T = \frac{3}{2}$	$T = \frac{1}{2}$
$\frac{3}{2}$	$\lvert p\pi^+\rangle$	
$\frac{1}{2}$	$\frac{1}{\sqrt{3}}(\lvert n\pi^+\rangle - \sqrt{2}\,\lvert p\pi^0\rangle)$	$\frac{1}{\sqrt{3}}(\sqrt{2}\,\lvert n\pi^+\rangle + \lvert p\pi^0\rangle)$
$-\frac{1}{2}$	$\frac{1}{\sqrt{3}}(\lvert p\pi^-\rangle + \sqrt{2}\,\lvert n\pi^0\rangle)$	$\frac{1}{\sqrt{3}}(\sqrt{2}\,\lvert p\pi^-\rangle - \lvert n\pi^0\rangle)$
$-\frac{3}{2}$	$\lvert n\pi^-\rangle$	

and for charge-exchange scattering,

$$F_{\text{ch. ex.}} = \frac{\sqrt{2}}{3}(F^{3/2} - F^{1/2}) \qquad \pi^- p \to \pi^0 n \quad \text{or} \quad \pi^+ n \to \pi^0 p \tag{3-10}$$

These three amplitudes are not independent. As is obvious from (3-10)

$$F_{\pi^+ p} = F_{\pi^- p} + \sqrt{2}\, F_{\text{ch. ex.}} \tag{3-11}$$

Such a relation provides a typical test of charge independence. As an equality among amplitudes it implies triangular inequalities among differential cross sections

$$\left| \sqrt{2}\left(\frac{d\sigma_{\text{ch. ex.}}}{d\Omega}\right)^{1/2} - \left(\frac{d\sigma_{\pi^- p}}{d\Omega}\right)^{1/2} \right| \le \left(\frac{d\sigma_{\pi^+ p}}{d\Omega}\right)^{1/2} \le \left(\frac{d\sigma_{\pi^- p}}{d\Omega}\right)^{1/2} + \sqrt{2}\left(\frac{d\sigma_{\text{ch. ex.}}}{d\Omega}\right)^{1/2} \tag{3-12}$$

$$\frac{d\sigma_{\pi^+ p}}{d\Omega} = |f^{3/2}|^2$$

$$\frac{d\sigma_{\pi^- p}}{d\Omega} = \tfrac{1}{9}(|f^{3/2}|^2 + 4|f^{1/2}|^2 + 4\,\mathrm{Re}\, f^{3/2*} f^{1/2})$$

and‡

‡ Capital and lower case letters are used according to (1-10) and (1-12).

$$\frac{d\sigma_{ch.\,ex.}}{d\Omega} = \tfrac{2}{9}(|f^{3/2}|^2 + |f^{1/2}|^2 - 2\,\mathrm{Re}\,f^{3/2\,*}f^{1/2})$$

The total $\pi^- p$ cross section (elastic + charge exchange) is then

$$\frac{d\sigma_-}{d\Omega} = \tfrac{1}{3}(|f^{3/2}|^2 + 2|f^{1/2}|^2)$$

We then obtain the total cross section in the isotopic spin $\frac{3}{2}$ and $\frac{1}{2}$ states as

$$\sigma_{3/2} = \sigma_+ \qquad \text{and} \qquad \sigma_{1/2} = \tfrac{1}{2}(3\sigma_- - \sigma_+) \tag{3-13}$$

defining $\mathbf{T}$ as $\mathbf{t} + \boldsymbol{\tau}/2$; eigenstates of $\mathbf{T}^2$ are eigenstates of $\mathbf{t}\cdot\boldsymbol{\tau}$ with eigenvalues $1(T = \frac{3}{2})$ and $-2(T = \frac{1}{2})$. Instead of two scattering amplitudes we may as well introduce a scattering operator in charge space:

$$F = F^{3/2}P_{3/2} + F^{1/2}P_{1/2}$$

where (3-14)

$$P_{3/2} = \frac{2 + \mathbf{t}\cdot\boldsymbol{\tau}}{3} \qquad \text{and} \qquad P_{1/2} = \frac{1 - \mathbf{t}\cdot\boldsymbol{\tau}}{3}$$

are, respectively, projection operators on the total isotopic spin $\frac{3}{2}$ and $\frac{1}{2}$ states.

If we specify the initial and final π-meson charge, the scattering operator becomes a 2×2 matrix in the nucleon charge subspace. By using the $|\pi_1\rangle$, $|\pi_2\rangle$, and $|\pi_3\rangle$ basis (3-4), we obtain

$$(\mathbf{t}\cdot\boldsymbol{\tau})_{ji} = i\epsilon_{ijk}\tau_k = \tfrac{1}{2}[\tau_i, \tau_j]$$

where i and j are the initial and final meson charge indices. Together with (3-14) this gives

$$[\tau_i, \tau_j] = 2(P_{3/2} - 2P_{1/2})_{ji}$$

and we also have

$$(P_{3/2} + P_{1/2})_{ji} = \delta_{ji}$$

The scattering operator is then also written

$$F_{ji} = \delta_{ji}F^{(+)} + \tfrac{1}{2}[\tau_j, \tau_i]F^{(-)} \tag{3-15}$$

and following (1-16) we write

$$A_{ji} = \delta_{ji} A^{(+)} + \tfrac{1}{2}[\tau_j, \tau_i] A^{(-)} \qquad B_{ji} = \delta_{ji} B^{(+)} + \tfrac{1}{2}[\tau_j, \tau_i] B^{(-)}$$

$F^{(+)}$ and $F^{(-)}$ are two new amplitudes which, expressed in terms of $F^{3/2}$ and $F^{1/2}$, read

$$F^{(+)} = \tfrac{1}{3}(2F^{3/2} + F^{1/2}) \qquad F^{(-)} = \tfrac{1}{3}(F^{1/2} - F^{3/2}) \tag{3-16}$$

As follows from (3-10)

$$F_{\pi^- p} = F^{(+)} + F^{(-)} \qquad F_{\pi^+ p} = F^{(+)} - F^{(-)} \qquad \text{and}$$

$$F_{\text{ch. ex.}} = -\sqrt{2}\, F^{(-)}$$

These new amplitudes are very useful to consider, since they are, respectively, even and odd with respect to the exchange of the initial and final π-meson charge index, $i \rightleftharpoons j$.

Now, if we consider π-nucleon scattering as shown in Fig. 1-3, the amplitude is invariant under the exchange $p_1 \rightleftharpoons -p_3$ and $i \rightleftharpoons j$.‡ As mentioned in Chapter 1, this is easily seen in perturbation theory. It is an important symmetry property called "crossing symmetry" which is true independently of perturbation theory. In this particular case s and u are exchanged; t does not change. $F^{(+)}$ and $F^{(-)}$ transform in a very simple way under crossing as follows from their definition (3-15).

$$F^{(\pm)}(s,t,u) = \pm F^{(\pm)}(u,t,s) \tag{3-17}$$

The two isotopic spin amplitudes do not transform as simply. Combining (3-16) and (3-17) we obtain the crossing matrix:

	$\frac{3}{2}$	$\frac{1}{2}$
$\frac{3}{2}$	$\frac{1}{3}$	$\frac{4}{3}$
$\frac{1}{2}$	$\frac{2}{3}$	$-\frac{1}{3}$

(3-18)

3–4 G-PARITY

Under rotation in charge space (a rotation of angle φ around the 2-axis, say) the proton and neutron states are transformed as follows:

‡ p_1 (and p_3) are the meson momenta; p_2 (and p_4), the nucleon momenta.

$$|p\rangle' = \cos\frac{\varphi}{2}\,|p\rangle + \sin\frac{\varphi}{2}\,|n\rangle$$
$$|n\rangle' = -\sin\frac{\varphi}{2}\,|p\rangle + \cos\frac{\varphi}{2}\,|n\rangle \tag{3-19}$$

The antiproton and antineutron are eigenstates of T_3 with eigenvalues $-\frac{1}{2}$ and $+\frac{1}{2}$ (3-2). Under the same rotation they would transform in the following way:

$$|\bar{p}\rangle' = \cos\frac{\varphi}{2}\,|\bar{p}\rangle + \sin\frac{\varphi}{2}\,|\bar{n}\rangle$$
$$|\bar{n}\rangle' = -\sin\frac{\varphi}{2}\,|\bar{p}\rangle + \cos\frac{\varphi}{2}\,|\bar{n}\rangle \tag{3-20}$$

If instead of $|\bar{p}\rangle$ and $|\bar{n}\rangle$, we choose $-|\bar{p}\rangle$ and $|\bar{n}\rangle$ as basic state vectors, we obtain for these new states the transformation law (3-19) written for the neutron and proton states as we should according to the pertinent values of T_3.

It is easy to check that the operator

$$G = Ce^{i\pi T_2} \tag{3-21}$$

where C is the charge conjugation operator, transforms $|p\rangle$ into $|\bar{n}\rangle$ and $|n\rangle$ into $-|\bar{p}\rangle$. The arbitrary phase introduced with charge conjugation is chosen to be the same for the proton and the neutron.

As a consequence it is obvious that, for nucleons, G commutes with T_2. It is easily verified that it commutes in fact with all three components of $\mathbf{T}$.

$$[G, T_i] = 0 \tag{3-22}$$

G is called the "G-parity operator."[9] It anticommutes with the baryonic charge and strangeness operators. It is often more convenient than C, since C does not commute with T^*.‡ Charge symmetry and charge conjugation invariance imply invariance under G for strong interaction processes.

Applied once more to $|\bar{n}\rangle$ (and $-|\bar{p}\rangle$), G gives $-|p\rangle$ (and $-|n\rangle$). With (3-22) it is easy to construct total isotopic spin 0 and 1 states for a nucleon-antinucleon system. One simply replaces $|p\rangle$ by $|\bar{n}\rangle$ and $|n\rangle$ by $-|\bar{p}\rangle$ in Table 3-2, giving Table 3-4. When G is applied to these states the baryonic number and the charge of the two particles are exchanged and one obtains an over-all factor $(-)^T$. If the two particles are in an eigenstate of orbital angular momentum

‡C anticommutes with T_3.

Table 3-4

T_3	T = 1	T = 0
1	$\|p\bar{n}\rangle$	
0	$\frac{1}{\sqrt{2}}(\|n\bar{n}\rangle - \|p\bar{p}\rangle)$	$-\frac{1}{\sqrt{2}}(\|p\bar{p}\rangle + \|n\bar{n}\rangle)$
−1	$\|n\bar{p}\rangle$	

and spin, their exchange introduces a factor $(-1)(-1)^{\ell}(-)^{S+1} = (-1)^{\ell+S}$, parity times spin exchange. The $N\bar{N}$ state is then an eigenstate of G with eigenvalue $(-1)^{\ell+S+T}$.

For a neutral system with a well-defined integer isotopic spin $e^{i\pi T_2}$ simply gives $(-)^T$, and we have $(N = S = 0)$

$$G = C(-1)^T \tag{3-23}$$

A neutral $N\bar{N}$ system in a well-defined angular momentum, and spin state is then in an eigenstate of C with eigenvalue $(-1)^{\ell+S}$. If it is odd under C, it is even (or odd) under G if its total isotopic spin is 1 (or 0). These are the two possiblities encountered for the photon $N\bar{N}$ vertex (a one-photon state is odd under C).

An eigenstate of G is said to have G-parity ± 1. We now apply the operator G to π-meson states. Under the transformation $e^{i\pi T_2}$

$$|\pi_1\rangle \to -|\pi_1\rangle \qquad |\pi_2\rangle \to |\pi_2\rangle \qquad |\pi_3\rangle \to -|\pi_3\rangle$$

Under C

$$|\pi^+\rangle \rightleftharpoons |\pi^-\rangle$$

$$|\pi_1\rangle \to |\pi_1\rangle \qquad |\pi_2\rangle \to -|\pi_2\rangle \qquad |\pi_3\rangle \to |\pi_3\rangle$$

assuming the same phase factor for the charged and neutral π-mesons. Altogether under G we find

$$|\pi\rangle \to -|\pi\rangle$$

and one also checks that for π-mesons as well

$$[G, T_i] = 0$$

A 1π-meson state is odd under G; an $n\pi$-meson state has obviously a G-parity $(-)^n$.

Because strong interactions are invariant under G, any process is forbidden in which only an odd number of π-mesons enters. A 3π-meson vertex is forbidden by Lorentz invariance. One cannot construct a pseudoscalar amplitude with three independent vectors. Processes involving any odd number of pions only are then further forbidden up to the order of electromagnetic corrections.

Let us finally consider the intermediate states between a virtual photon and a $N\bar{N}$ system. For $T = 1$, we have $G = +1$ and hence 2π, 4π, 6π, ... mesons. For $T = 0$, $G = -1$ and 3π, 5π, ... mesons. This is an important result in the analysis of the nucleon form factors.

Selection rules for $N\bar{N}$ annihilation into pions are also easily obtained from Table 3-4.

We have considered in detail only systems made up of pions and nucleons. The formalism is extended in a straightforward way to any charge multiplet. We shall deal, later on, with several examples when we consider the newly discovered mesons.

4

PHENOMENOLOGICAL ANALYSIS OF PION-NUCLEON SCATTERING

4–1 PHASE SHIFTS AND INELASTICITY PARAMETERS

This chapter presents a brief review of the experimental situation for π-nucleon scattering. We first consider elastic scattering. As shown previously, all experimental results can be expressed in terms of two amplitudes $f_1^T(W, \cos\theta)$ and $f_2^T(W, \cos\theta)$ for each value of the total isotopic spin: $T = \frac{1}{2}$ and $\frac{3}{2}$. Each amplitude can further be expressed in terms of partial-wave amplitudes in the following way:

$$f_1^T(W, \cos\theta) = \sum_\ell f_{\ell_+}^T(W)\, P'_{\ell+1}(\cos\theta) + f_{\ell-}^T\, P'_{\ell-1}(\cos\theta)$$
$$f_2^T(W, \cos\theta) = \sum_\ell \left(f_{\ell_-}^T(W) - f_{\ell_+}^T(W)\right) P'_\ell(\cos\theta) \tag{4-1}$$

Such expansions are very useful for two reasons.

First, following a classical argument we expect that an interaction of range r ($r \simeq 10^{-13}$ cm) should mainly affect partial waves with values of ℓ less than $q \cdot r$, where q is the center-of-mass momentum. For a π-meson of 200 MeV one should not expect D or higher waves to be at all important and only three partial-wave amplitudes can be retained in (4-1), namely, f_{0+}, f_{1-}, and f_{1+} for both isotopic spin states.

Second, π-nucleon cross sections up to 2 Bev show large peaks. If these peaks corresponded to resonances, π-nucleon scattering would be dominated by the behavior of a small number of partial-wave amplitudes, though the number of partial waves, to include a priori as important, increases rapidly with energy (all waves up to G-waves at 1 BeV).

Below the threshold for production of one π-meson, π-nucleon scattering is purely elastic. The partial-wave amplitudes are expressed in terms of real phase shifts as

$$f^T_{\ell j} = \frac{1}{q} \exp\left(i\,\delta^T_{\ell j}\right) \sin \delta^T_{\ell j} = \frac{\exp\left(2i\,\delta^T_{\ell j} - 1\right)}{2iq} \tag{4-2}$$

At higher energies, unitarity is no longer expressed in such a simple way and we write

$$f^T_{\ell j} = \frac{\eta^T_{\ell j} - 1}{2iq} \tag{4-3}$$

with

$$|\eta^T_{\ell j}| \leq 1 \tag{4-4}$$

We finally write

$$\eta^T_{\ell j} = \rho^T_{\ell j} \exp\left(2i\,\delta^T_{\ell j}\right) \tag{4-5}$$

where δ is a real number and ρ is the inelasticity parameter, $0 \leq \rho \leq 1$.

For $\rho = 1$ the scattering is purely elastic, for $\rho = 0$ there is complete absorption, and pure shadow scattering.

The elastic and inelastic, partial-wave cross sections read

$$\begin{aligned} \sigma^j_{el} &= \frac{\pi}{q_2}\left(j + \tfrac{1}{2}\right) \left| 1 - \eta_{\ell j} \right|^2 \\ \sigma^j_{inel} &= \frac{\pi}{q^2}\left(j + \tfrac{1}{2}\right)\left(1 - \rho^2_{\ell j}\right) \end{aligned} \tag{4-6}$$

Only three charge amplitudes are readily interesting. They correspond, respectively, to $\pi^+p \to \pi^+p$, $\pi^-p \to \pi^-p$, and $\pi^-p \to \pi^0 n$ scattering. These amplitudes $f\pi^+p$, $f\pi^-p$, and $f^{ch.ex}$ are expressed in terms of the two total isotopic spin amplitudes in the following way (3-10):

$$f_{\ell j}^{\pi^+ p} = f_{\ell j}^{3/2}$$

$$f_{\ell j}^{\pi^- p} = \tfrac{1}{3}\left(f_{\ell j}^{3/2} + 2f_{\ell j}^{1/2}\right) \tag{4-7}$$

$$f_{\ell j}^{\mathrm{ch.ex}} = \frac{\sqrt{2}}{3}\left(f_{\ell j}^{3/2} - f_{\ell j}^{1/2}\right)$$

The phase shifts and inelasticity parameters are the convenient parameters for analyzing the experimental data.

4–2 PION-NUCLEON SCATTERING BELOW 300 MeV

Up to 300 MeV inelastic effects are negligible and only s and p waves should be important. This leaves six parameters only‡

$$\delta_{0\,1/2}^{1/2}, \delta_{1\,1/2}^{1/2}, \delta_{1\,3/2}^{1/2} \qquad \text{and} \qquad \delta_{0\,1/2}^{3/2}, \delta_{1\,1/2}^{3/2}, \delta_{1\,3/2}^{3/2}$$

Relations (4-1) reduce to

$$f_1 = \frac{1}{q}\left(e^{i\delta_{0\,1/2}} \sin \delta_{0\,1/2} + 3 \cos \theta \, e^{i\delta_{1\,3/2}} \sin \delta_{1\,3/2}\right)$$

$$f_2 = \frac{1}{q}\left(e^{i\delta_{1\,1/2}} \sin \delta_{1\,1/2} - e^{i\delta_{1\,3/2}} \sin \delta_{1\,3/2}\right) \tag{4-8}$$

for each value of the isotopic spin. The center-of-mass differential cross sections, and polarizations, are readily obtained from relations (2-25) and (2-27) together with (4-7).

For instance, the $\pi^+ p$ differential cross section reads

$$\frac{d\sigma_+}{d\Omega} = \frac{1}{q^2}(A + B \cos \theta + C \cos^2 \theta) \tag{4-9}$$

with

$$A = \sin^2 \delta_{0\,1/2} + \sin^2 \delta_{1\,1/2} + \sin^2 \delta_{1\,3/2}$$
$$- 2 \sin \delta_{1\,3/2} \sin \delta_{1\,1/2} \cos (\delta_{1\,3/2} - \delta_{1\,1/2})$$

$$B = 4 \cos (\delta_{1\,3/2} - \delta_{0\,1/2}) \sin \delta_{0\,1/2} \sin \delta_{1\,3/2}$$
$$+ 2 \cos (\delta_{1\,1/2} - \delta_{0\,1/2}) \sin \delta_{0\,1/2} \sin \delta_{1\,1/2}$$

‡They are often referred to as α_1, α_{11}, α_{13} and α_3, α_{31}, α_{33}.

$$C = 3\sin^2\delta_{1\,3/2} + 6\sin\delta_{1\,3/2}\sin\delta_{1\,1/2} \times \cos(\delta_{1\,3/2} - \delta_{1\,1/2})$$

and the total cross section

$$\sigma_+ = \frac{4\pi}{q^2}(A + \tfrac{1}{3}C) = \frac{4\pi}{q^2}(\sin^2\delta_{0\,1/2} + \sin^2\delta_{1\,1/2} + 2\sin^2\delta_{1\,3/2}) \qquad (4\text{-}10)$$

In this case, scattering occurs in a pure isotopic spin state: $T = \frac{3}{2}$.

Experimental results in this energy range are summarized in Figs. 4-1 and 4-2. Figure 4-1 gives the total π^+p cross section as well as the total π^-p cross section. Figure 4-2 shows the variation with energy of the A, B, and C coefficients of (4-9) which provides a good fit to the differential cross section.

The prominent feature is the large peak at 190 MeV (total π-nucleon center-of-mass energy of 1238 MeV). As a resonance in π-nucleon interaction this peak has to correspond to a complete set of quantum numbers—isotopic spin, spin, and parity. The occurrence of the peak in π^+p scattering implies $T = \frac{3}{2}$. Furthermore, the σ_+, σ_-, and $\sigma_{ch.ex.}$ cross sections at 190 MeV are almost in the ratio 9:2:1 which would correspond to $T = \frac{3}{2}$ alone even for π^-p scattering.

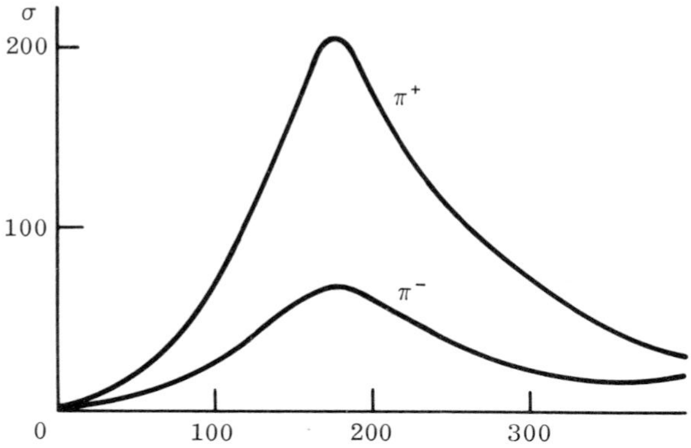

Figure 4-1

The π^+ laboratory energy is given in million electron volts, and the total cross section is given in millibarns.

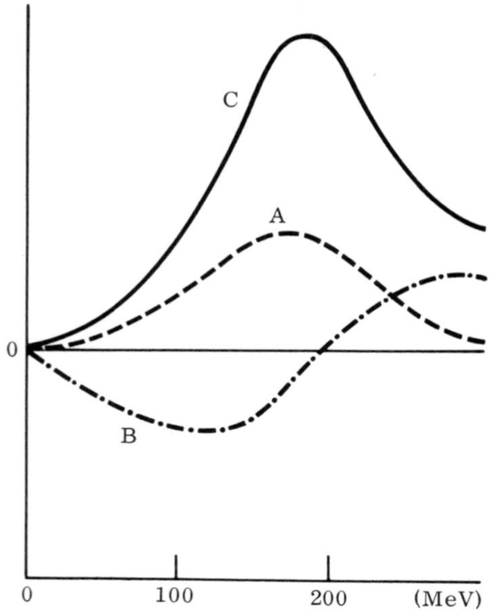

Figure 4-2

The simplest assumption is that only one particular phase shift is large (in fact goes through 90°) at 190 MeV. Since $8\pi/q^2 = 190$ mb at 190 MeV, (4-10) implies that the resonance should occur in the $p^{3/2}$ state. One then expects that $C \sim 3A$ and that B goes through 0 in the resonance region. This is well verified as shown by Fig. 4-2. This corresponds to the Fermi set of phase shifts which can be summarized as follows:

> There is a resonance in the $p^{3/2}$, $T = \frac{3}{2}$ state, $\delta^{3/2}_{0\ 1/2}$ is small and negative, $\delta^{3/2}_{1\ 1/2}$ is small.[10]

Nevertheless, it is impossible to make conclusions on the basis of the total and differential cross sections alone and, in fact, an equally good fit to those data can be obtained with the Yang set of phase shifts. It assumes a resonance in the $p^{3/2}$ state at 190 MeV but also a resonance in the $p^{1/2}$ state at 130 MeV. The rapid rise of $\delta_{1\ 3/2}$ at 130 MeV would not allow the $p^{1/2}$ resonance to manifest itself as a peak in the cross section.

On the other hand, the predictions of the static theory[11] and the successes of the dispersion theory clearly show that the Fermi set of phase shifts gives the correct picture for π-nucleon scattering below 300 MeV.

At this point it is worth mentioning ambiguities that arise when one tries to fit differential cross sections alone in terms of phase shifts. To this end let us consider the expression obtained for the differential cross section, for a nonpolarized target

$$\frac{d\sigma}{d\Omega} = \frac{1}{2} \sum_{(\lambda)} \sum_{jj'} (2j+1)(2j'+1) \,\mathrm{Re}\left\{f^{j}_{\lambda\lambda'}\, f^{j'^*}_{\lambda\lambda'}\right\} (-1)^{\lambda-\lambda'}$$

$$\times \sum_{\ell} C(jj'^{\ell} \mid \lambda, -\lambda)\, C(jj'^{\ell} \mid \lambda', -\lambda')\, P_{\ell}(\cos\theta) \tag{2-25}$$

with

$$2f^{j}_{++} = f_{\ell_+} + f'_{(\ell+1)_-}$$

$$2f^{j}_{-+} = f_{\ell_+} - f_{(\ell+1)_-}$$

Now, changing the sign of all phase shifts, changes the sign of the imaginary part, but does not change the real part of the products $f^{j} f^{j'^*}$. This follows immediately from (4-2), and shows that the differential cross section does not change when all phase shifts are reversed.

To obtain the sign of the phase shifts, one has to analyze interferences with Coulomb scattering. With Wigner's theorem, we also know that the phase of the $p^{3/2}$ partial wave has to increase at the resonance.

Another general ambiguity is the Minami ambiguity. The differential cross section does not change if, for all values of j, the two phase shifts (corresponding to opposite parities) are interchanged. In other words, ℓ_+ and $(\ell+1)_-$ are interchanged for all j. This is evident from (2-25); f^{j}_{++} does not change, f^{j}_{-+} changes sign. Since the terms that appear in the angular distribution correspond to the same helicities, $d\sigma/d\Omega$ obviously does not change.

The polarization of the recoil nucleon (with a nonpolarized target) changes sign as shown by (2-26) under this transformation.

4–3 PION-NUCLEON SCATTERING AT HIGHER ENERGIES

Though a large amount of data is already available it is not possible to get more than a general understanding. Many more partial waves have to be considered, and inelastic collisions play an important part which is still difficult to analyze. It seems fair to separate two regions. Up to approximately 2 BeV, the total cross sections

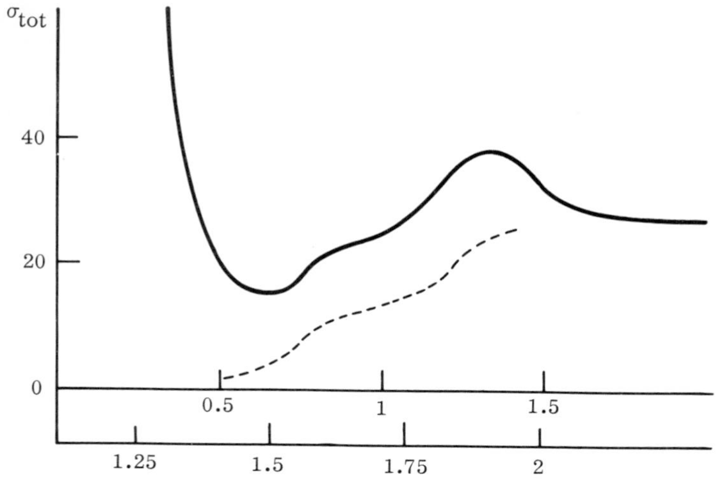

Figure 4-3
The π^+ laboratory energy is given in billion electron volts (upper scale), and the second scale gives the center-of-mass total energy in billion electron volts. The total cross section is given in millibarns. The dashed curve represents the inelastic cross section.

are dominated by well-marked peaks that are most likely resonances. This is the resonance region. Above 2 BeV, π-nucleon scattering is dominated by inelastic processes. The σ_+ and σ_- cross sections‡ seem to tend toward a common limit of the order of 25 mb, and the elastic differential cross section shows the strong forward peak expected from shadow scattering. This could already be the asymptotic region. We shall confine ourselves to analyzing the present experimental situation in the resonance region.

The total cross sections for π^+p and π^-p scattering above 300 MeV are shown in Figs. 4-3 and 4-4. The prominent feature is the presence of very marked peaks.[12]

The simplest idea is to associate resonances to such peaks. One should then try to obtain a consistent picture with well-defined quantum numbers associated to each resonance. We shall discuss in detail only the second and third peaks in π^-p scattering. They both correspond to $T = \frac{1}{2}$.

Let us first assume that they are both resonances. From the total cross section, the angular momentum of the third resonance should then be taken as $\frac{5}{2}$ or $\frac{7}{2}$. The angular distribution in the resonance region is, however, fitted with a polynomial expression

‡They are now, respectively, the π^+p and π^-p total cross section.

$$\frac{d\sigma}{d\Omega} = \sum_n a_n \cos^n \theta \qquad \text{with } n \leq 5$$

At a given energy, this would not be enough to rule out an angular momentum higher than $\frac{5}{2}$ but the variation with energy of the a_5 coefficient allows $J = \frac{5}{2}$ to be taken with confidence.

The total cross section is well fitted with a fairly constant background and a Breit-Wigner formula. The value at the resonance for the partial-wave cross section (40 ± 5 mb) gives an inelasticity parameter $\rho = 0.8 \pm 0.2$. This is high as compared to an average inelasticity parameter of the order of 0.6, found for the other $T = \frac{1}{2}$ partial waves.[13] The partial-wave total cross section at the resonance is

$$\sigma^j_{tot} = \frac{\pi}{q^2}(2j + 1)(1 + \rho)$$

The occurrence of the peak seems then to be disconnected from inelastic effects. Such conclusions are still enforced by the analysis of forward dispersion relations.[14] For the second peak, on the contrary, it does not seem at all that one almost elastic wave singles itself out. The best evidence for the angular momentum is taken

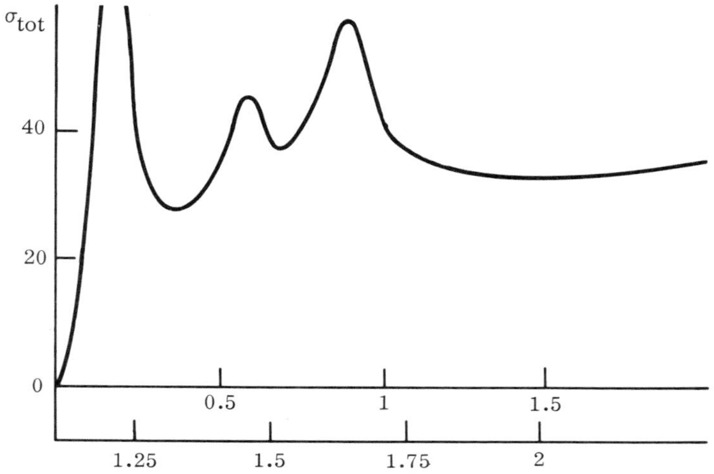

Figure 4-4

The π^- laboratory energy is given in billion electron volts (upper scale), and the lower scale gives the center-of-mass total energy in billion electron volts. The total cross section is given in millibarns. The masses of the second and third resonances are, respectively, 1515 MeV and 1685 MeV.

Recent experiments have been concerned with particular inelastic channels such as $\pi^{\pm}p \rightarrow \pi^{\pm} + \pi^{\circ} + p$. Peaks also seem to occur in the pertinent cross section at the right energies.[19] This supports a resonance picture.

As a resonance, the $\pi^{+}p$ peak at 1300 MeV should most likely have spin $\frac{7}{2}$.

Obviously more work is needed on phase shift analysis above 300 MeV. This is a difficult task, but the use of polarized targets could help a great deal.

4–4 INELASTIC PROCESSES

Up to 1 BeV, inelastic processes seem to be dominated by the first resonance. There is mainly production of one π-meson, both π-mesons interacting with the nucleon through the $p^{3/2}$ resonance. In fact, in this energy region, events for which the nucleon and either of the two π-mesons have a center-of-mass total energy of 1200-1300 MeV have a high statistical weight and one should expect the resonance to be important at least through final-state interactions.[20] The isobaric model where one assumes the inelastic process to be merely

$$\pi + N \rightarrow N^{*} + \pi \tag{4-12}$$

where N^{*} stands for the first resonance,[21] is successful in fitting the pion spectra. Figure 4-6 gives, for instance, the π° spectrum obtained with 900 MeV incident π^{+} on protons.

The branching ratio $R = \sigma(p\pi^{+}\pi^{0})/\sigma(n\pi^{+}\pi^{+})$ is, however, found to vary with energy and to be only 3.2 ± 0.5 at 900 MeV[22] as compared to the value 6.5, expected from a two-body reaction (4-12) in the $T = \frac{3}{2}$ state. The "initial" production mechanism, which is almost smeared out in the spectra and angular distributions by the resonance interaction in the final state, is probably more complicated than (4-12), and since even higher waves show a small inelasticity parameter, peripheral interactions should be important.[23,24]

Above 1 BeV, production of 2, 3, . . . π-mesons becomes important. Events for which the nucleon and one pion have the N^{*} resonance energy do not any longer have a large statistical weight. The first resonance loses some of its importance but 2 and 3 π-resonances start showing up clearly. They are discussed in detail in the next chapter.

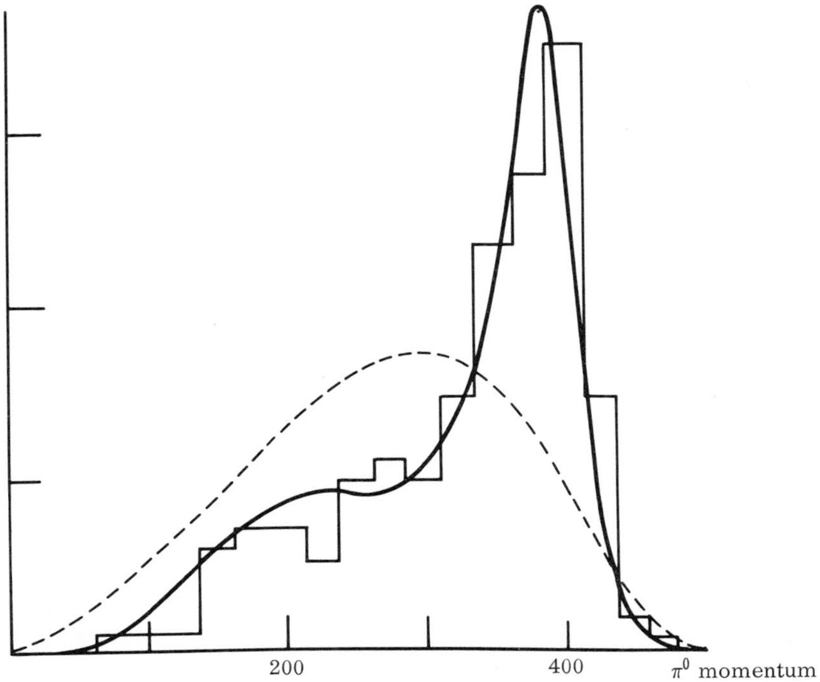

Figure 4-6

The π^0 momentum is given in million electron volts. The solid line is the prediction of the isobaric model; the dashed line represents the phase space distribution.

4–5 STRANGE ISOBARS

In order to compare with the π-nucleon case we now briefly discuss strange isobars. From now on, we identify peak and resonance and say that several resonances or isobars have been found in π-hyperon interactions. Such interactions are often studied through their effect, as final-state interactions, in reactions where a hyperon and a π-meson are produced together with one extra particle. For instance:

$$K^- p \to \Lambda + \pi^+ + \pi^- \tag{4-13}$$

A resonance then shows up as the N^* resonance in a $\pi + N \to 2\pi + N$ reaction just considered. Figure 4-7 shows the mass spectrum observed in reaction (4-13) for incident K^- of 1.22 BeV/c. The solid curve is obtained assuming that the reaction proceeds only like

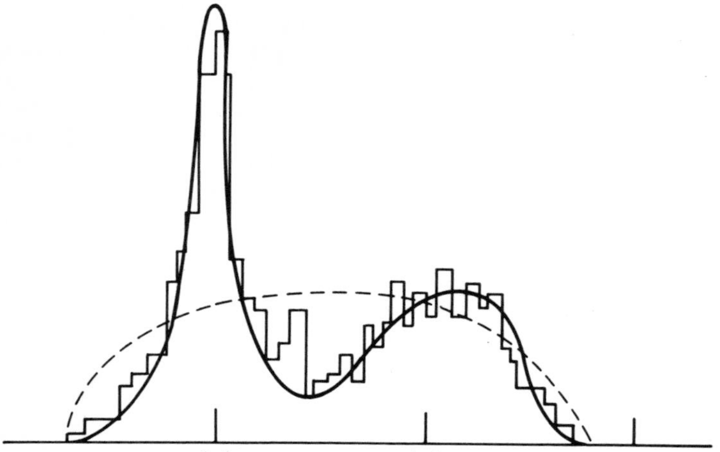

Figure 4-7
The histogram can be considered as the projection of Fig. 1-2.

$K^-p \rightarrow Y_1^* + \pi$, where the Y_1^* would be a particle of mass 1385 Mev and width 50 MeV. This is to be compared with the solid line fit in Fig. 4-6.

Spin and parity can be obtained through the analysis of the angular distribution of the decay hyperon together with its polarization, which is readily obtained from its decay asymmetry. Finally, if the strangeness-1 hyperon isobar energy is high enough, it shows up as a resonance in the $\overline{K}$-nucleon system. We shall merely list the strange isobars (Table 4-1) that are considered as certain at present together with the most likely spin and parity assignments.[25]

Table 4-1

Name	S	T	Mass and width, MeV	Spin parity
Y_0^*	−1	0	1405, 50	$\frac{1}{2}^-$ (?)
Y_0^{**}	−1	0	1520, 15	$\frac{3}{2}^-$
Y_0^{***}	−1	0	1815, 100	$>\frac{3}{2}$
Y_1^*	−1	1	1385, 50	$\frac{3}{2}^+$
Y_1^{**}	−1	1	1660, 50	
Ξ^*	−2	$\frac{1}{2}$	1532, 7	$\frac{3}{2}^+$

In the framework of the octet model of unitary symmetry[26] the Y_0^{**} and Y_1^{**} could be associated with the second π-nucleon resonance $(\frac{3}{2}^-)$ in an octuplet, together with a new $\Xi\pi$ d-wave resonance still to be found. The Y_1^*, Ξ^*, and first π-nucleon resonance, $N^*(\frac{3}{2}^+)$, could be accommodated in at least a decuplet with one still missing particle, Ω^-, with isotopic spin 0 and strangeness -3. The equal mass splitting in the decuplet would give a mass of 1685 MeV for Ω^-.

[*Note added in proof:* A baryon with charge -1 and strangeness -3 has now been discovered.[63] Its mass is as predicted.]

5

NEW MESONS

5–1 PRODUCTION OF NEW PARTICLES

The striking feature of inelastic collisions in which several π-mesons are produced is that there is a high probability to find two, or three, of these π-mesons with a well-defined total center-of-mass energy. This can be understood as the result of final-state interaction between π-mesons. This should be important if there is a 2π- or 3π-meson resonance (i.e., a pole of the scattering amplitude in the energy variable). In this case it is just as fair to say that a new meson (the resonance) is produced in the collision and then decays into 2π- or 3π-mesons.

Mass distribution for groups of π-mesons reveals such new particles in many different reactions in which π-mesons are produced: π-proton (or π-deuteron) collisions (mainly above 1 BeV), antiproton annihilation (mainly annihilation at rest), K^--nucleon collisions.... Two such resonances have also been found in the $K + \pi$ system and one in the $K\bar{K}$ system.

For the purpose of illustration, Fig. 5-1 shows the mass distribution observed in the $\pi^+ d \rightarrow p + p + \pi^+ + \pi^- + \pi^0$ reaction. The ω- and η-mesons are clearly seen.

The new particles which have been found so far and which will be discussed in some details are the following[27]:

the ω found in the $\pi^+\pi^-\pi^0$ system at an energy of 790 MeV ($5.6\,\mu$) and a width $\Gamma < 10$ MeV[28]

the η also found in the $\pi^+\pi^-\pi^0$ system at an energy of 550 MeV ($4\,\mu$) with $\Gamma < 7$ MeV[29]

the ρ found in the 2π system ($\pi^+\pi^0$, $\pi^+\pi^-$, $\pi^-\pi^0$) at an energy of 750 MeV and a width of the order of 100 MeV[30]

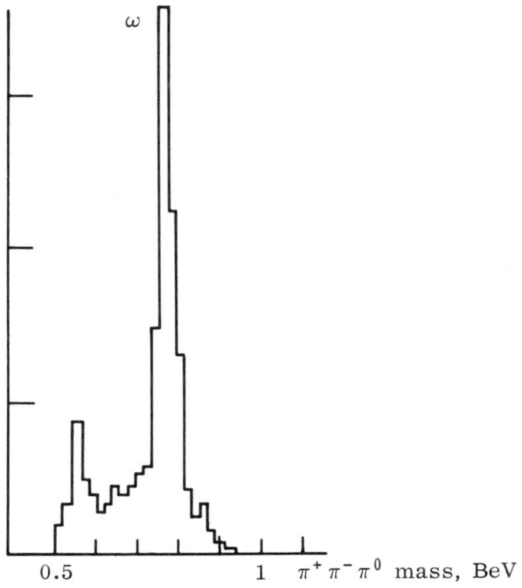

Figure 5-1

the f_0 also found in the 2π system ($\pi^+ \pi^-$) at 1250 MeV with a fairly large width (100 MeV?)[31]

the φ found in the $K\overline{K}$ system at 1020 MeV with a small width $\Gamma \simeq 2$ MeV[32]

the K^* found in the $K + \pi$ system at 885 MeV with a width of 50 MeV[33] and another $K + \pi$ particle at 730 MeV with a narrow width

These particles are produced with cross sections of the order of a millibarn. Production must then occur through strong interaction, and each particle has to correspond to a complete set of quantum number, spin and parity, as well as isotopic spin, and G-parity for the nonstrange ones; and this, even if their decay is purely electromagnetic. They should manifest themselves in other channels (according to the quantum number assignment). The π-meson systems mentioned together with these new particles are simply the ones in which they were first discovered.

We now briefly discuss for each one of them how the quantum number assignment has been achieved.

5–2 THE ω-MESON

The ω is easily observed in the $\pi^+ \pi^- \pi^0$ system in reactions in which other charge configurations for 3π-mesons also occur ($p\bar{p} \to 5\pi$, $\pi^+ d \to p, p + 3\pi$). Since the ω is found only in the neutral system its isotopic spin must be 0.

If its decay is a strong-interaction process the 3 π-mesons are in a T = 0 state which has to be

$$\frac{1}{\sqrt{6}} \epsilon_{\alpha\beta\alpha} \phi^{\alpha}(1) \phi^{\beta}(2) \phi^{\gamma}(3)$$

It is the only possible isotopic spin scalar, linear in the 3 π-meson fields. Since it is totally antisymmetric, when any two of the π-mesons are exchanged, the decay amplitude should also be totally antisymmetric since we have three bosons. If the ω is a vector particle it should read

$$G\epsilon_{\mu\nu\sigma\rho} B^{\mu} p_1^{\nu} p_2^{\sigma} p_3^{\rho} \tag{5-1}$$

where B is the polarization vector of ω; p_1, p_2, and p_3 the π-meson momenta. It has to be a pseudoscalar since 3π-mesons are produced in the decay and this is the most general one. G is an arbitrary function of the momenta which is Lorentz invariant and symmetrical with respect to the exchange of any two of the π. A convenient set of variables to introduce consists of the squares of the center-of-mass energies of each π-meson pair,

$$s = -(p_1 + p_2)^2 \qquad t = -(p_2 + p_3)^2 \qquad u = -(p_2 + p_3)^2 \tag{5-2}$$

with

$$s + t + u = M^2 + 3\mu^2$$

M is the ω mass. G reads G(s,t,u) and is symmetrical by exchange of s, t, and u.

The ω cannot be a scalar particle since such a particle would not decay into 3π. It is a requirement of Lorentz invariance. One needs at least four independent vectors to construct a pseudoscalar decay amplitude.

It could be a pseudoscalar. The decay amplitude would then be a scalar, and since it has to be antisymmetrical the most general form would read

$$G(s,t,u)(s - u)(u - t)(t - s) \tag{5-3}$$

where G is still an arbitrary symmetrical function.

For a pseudovector ω, we obtain

$$G(s,t,u)B \cdot (p_1(u - t) + p_2(s - u) + p_3(t - s)) \quad (5\text{-}4)$$

Now consider the decay probability associated to each of these amplitudes. A convenient way to analyze the data is to use a Dalitz plot. Each decay event is represented as a point on a triangular graph; its distances to the sides being equal to the 3π-meson kinetic energies. Now it is easy to see that each decay amplitude considered implies a particular pattern for the distribution of events. This is illustrated by Fig. 5-2. Conservation of energy and momentum requires all events to be inside a curve that limits the so-called physical region. As shown in Chapter 1, a constant amplitude gives a uniformly covered physical region.

For a vector particle, the density must go to zero on the edge of the physical region (whenever the 3π momenta are colinear in the ω rest system). For a pseudovector particle it is zero whenever two momenta are equal (the third pion comes out with its maximum energy) or when $s = t = u$, i.e., at the center of the diagram. For a pseudoscalar particle it is zero whenever $s = t$ or $t = u$ or $u = s$, hence on the 3-symmetry axis of the triangle. This complicated pattern comes from the conservation of isotopic spin and the boson nature of the π-meson. This is obvious from (5-1), (5-4), and (5-3).

It is legitimate to take G as constant. This will become evident later. The vector assignment leads then to a density maximum at the center and falling to zero toward the edge. This is clearly different from what is expected from a pseudoscalar or a pseudovector (neglecting higher spins for the sake of the argument) and agrees very well with experiment.[28] Patterns expected when isotopic spin conservation is violated are discussed later. They also are much different.

Figure 5-2 shows the three patterns, respectively, expected from a vector, pseudovector, and pseudoscalar particle when the 3π decay is a strong-interaction process. The heavy curve (or dots) indicate the region where the density has to go to zero.

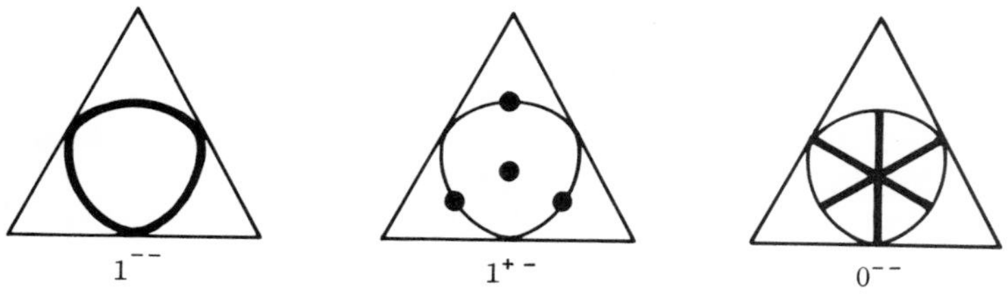

Figure 5-2

The ω is then a vector particle which decays into 3π-mesons through strong interactions. Its isotopic spin is zero and G-parity obviously (-1). A convenient notation is $0\ (1^{--})\ T\,(J^{PG})$. A question remains though. Why is the ω so narrow? A much larger width would a priori be expected from a strong-interaction decay. The decay amplitude (5-1) has, however, a structure such that G must have the dimension of a mass to the power -3. In any dynamical calculation this mass will appear as the inverse range of the decay interaction.

If the decay interaction has an inverse range large as compared to the average pion momentum, the ratio appears to the sixth power in the rate and will considerably slow down the decay. In other words (5-1) implies that each π-meson is produced at least in a p-wave with respect to either of the other two, and the small width of the ω is simply a result of centrifugal barrier effects. Dynamical calculations have been done.[34] No more than a rough approximation can be obtained but they all converge to a width of the order of 0.5 MeV, when assuming an a priori reasonable ω coupling. [*Note added in proof:* The larger width (9 ± 2 MeV) now found[64] implies that the ω is much more strongly coupled than one would expect for an octet member in unitary symmetry. This does not modify the calculated $\pi^0\gamma/3\pi$ branching ratio.]

Nonconstant terms in G correspond to higher partial waves for which centrifugal barrier effects are even more pronounced.

Since the 3π decay rate is so reduced by the centrifugal barrier, one expects other decay modes to be observable. Electromagnetic decay modes are a priori reduced by a factor‡ α or α^2, but some of them are not affected by the centrifugal barrier or, at least, much less than the 3π decay mode.

The most important should be the $\pi^0\gamma$ mode. The decay amplitude reads

$$G\epsilon_{\mu\nu\sigma\rho}\,A^{\mu}\,B^{\nu}\,p^{\sigma}\,k^{\rho} \tag{5-5}$$

p and k are the pion and photon momenta, and A is the polarization vector of the photon. G is now a constant of order e, with the dimension of an inverse mass. The centrifugal barrier effect is then quite small and this may compensate for the electromagnetic nature of the decay. Estimates of the $\pi^0\gamma/\pi^+\pi^-\pi^0$ branching ratio give 0.2. This agrees with the ω seen as a missing mass with a branching ratio, neutrals/$\pi^+\pi^-\pi^0$ of 0.21 ± 0.075.[35]

The ω is odd under charge conjugation [$C = G(-1)^T$ for a neutral state], and the decay into any number of π^0 is forbidden. A decay into 2γ is also forbidden and $\pi^0\gamma$ is then almost the only neutral mode.

A $\pi^+\pi^-$ decay mode is a priori of order α^2. Since it is at least a

---

‡ $\alpha = \dfrac{e^2}{\hbar c} = \dfrac{1}{137}$.

second-order electromagnetic process, one would expect it to be very small as compared to the $\pi^0\gamma$ mode if the ρ were not almost at the same energy. $\pi^+\pi^-$ interaction in final state is very strong and gives a large enhancement. This agrees with the branching ratio $\pi^+\pi^-/\pi^+\pi^-\pi^0 = 0.048 \pm 0.012$ found experimentally.[36] $\pi^+\pi^-\gamma$, $\pi^0\pi^0\gamma$, and e^+e^- are other modes which could come out with branching ratio of the order of at most 1 per cent.

5–3 THE η-MESON

As for the ω, the T = 0 assignment comes from the nonobservation of any similar effect in other charge configurations. The neutral decay modes are dominant. The branching ratio, neutrals/$\pi^+\pi^-\pi^0$ is of the order of 3. Following the preceding argument this would be expected from a vector particle of a lower mass than the ω (550 MeV instead of 790 MeV). The Dalitz plot is, however, found to be uniform in clear disagreement with any of the previously considered patterns. By giving up strong interactions, we have a priori a factor α^2 for the $\pi^+\pi^-\pi^0$ decay, but the extremely strong centrifugal barrier effect, found for a pseudoscalar particle, for instance, was due to the conservation of isotopic spin. If it does not hold, the 3π-mesons can be produced in an S-wave, and the decay amplitude is simply a constant. The G-parity has to be +1 so that the η be even under charge conjugation. Otherwise the π^+ and π^- could not be in an S-wave and the Dalitz plot would not be uniform.

This leads to a pseudoscalar η with positive G = 1 parity. The narrow width now comes from the electromagnetic nature of the decay. The actual width should be much less than 1 KeV. Even with violation of isotopic spin conservation, the decay amplitude‡ for a vector would be $G_0 \epsilon_{\mu\nu\sigma\rho} B^\mu p_1^\nu p_2^\sigma p_3^\rho$ or $G_0 \epsilon_{\mu\nu\sigma\rho} B^\mu p_1^\nu p_2^\sigma p_3^\rho (s - t)$ with G-parity −1 and +1. For a pseudovector one would have $G_0 B \cdot p_{\pi_0}$ $(s - t)$ or $G_0 B \cdot p_{\pi_0}$ according to whether G-parity is −1 or +1. All four would lead to patterns quite different from the uniform density found.

With the $0(0^{-+})$ assignment, the 2π decay is forbidden by Lorentz invariance. A 4π decay is forbidden (or almost) by conservation of energy. The neutral decay mode should then correspond to $\pi^0\pi^0\pi^0$ and 2γ. In fact, they have been observed recently.[37]

The $\gamma\gamma$ and $3\pi^0$ decay rates are found to be almost equal. The $3\pi^0/\pi^+\pi^-\pi^0$ branching ratio is then close to 1.5, a higher limit obtained from isotopic spin arguments.

---

‡ All amplitudes are written in such a way that the lowest-power term in G_0 is symmetrical in s, t, and u. A different G_0 is, of course, expected in each case.

A decay mode which should be a priori important is $\pi^+\pi^-\gamma$ ($\pi^0\pi^0\gamma$ is forbidden by C invariance). Roughly speaking one expects this rate to be of the order of α instead of α^2. It should be remarked, however, that the 2π must be in a state odd under C hence at least in a p-wave. The decay amplitudes reads

$$G_0(s,t,u)\,\epsilon_{\mu\nu\sigma\rho}A^{\mu}p_1^{\nu}p_2^{\sigma}p_3^{\rho}$$

where G_0 is a symmetrical function with respects to s and t ($\pi^+\pi^-$ exchange). Centrifugal barrier effects could slow down this process and explain the observed branching ratio $\pi^+\pi^-\gamma/\pi^+\pi^-\pi^0 = 0.26 \pm 0.08$.[38] The decay of the ω into $\eta + \pi$ is forbidden, even for electromagnetic interactions.

5–4 THE ρ-MESON

The ρ-meson appears as a broad resonance in the 2π system. Its observation in the $\pi^+\pi^0$, $\pi^+\pi^-$, and $\pi^-\pi^0$ charge states only, gives an isotopic spin assignment T = 1. Its spin is then odd. It shows up strongly in $\pi + N \to 2\pi + N$ reactions, especially above 1 BeV where the N^* production is no longer the prominent feature. It appears in an even stronger way on mass distributions when the events where the nucleon takes a small momentum transfer ($|t| \leq 10\mu^2$, say) are considered.

ρ production in such a reaction mainly occurs through a peripheral interaction. The simplest process corresponds to the graph of Fig. 5-3. At the upper vertex appears $\pi\pi$ scattering. As will be shown later (Chapter 7) one has the following relations:

$$\sigma_{\pi\pi}(\omega) = \lim_{t\to\mu^2}\left\{\frac{2\pi q^2(t-\mu^2)^2}{(g^2/4\pi)(t^2/4m^2)\,\omega\sqrt{(\omega^2/4)-\mu^2}} \times \frac{\partial^2\sigma}{\partial t\,\partial\omega^2}\right\} \tag{5-6}$$

According to this equation, extrapolation at $t = \mu^2$ yields the $\pi\pi$ cross section at the $\pi\pi$ center-of-mass energy ω. This extrapolation being helped by the fact that (5-3) is actually the important reaction mechanism. At present, data are, however, not precise enough to be extrapolated safely. It has been assumed then that for events with low $|t|$ the process shown on Fig. 5-3 is the only one and relation (5-6) is then used for negative t. The $\pi\pi$ cross section obtained through this procedure shows a peak at an energy of 750 MeV. The cross section at the peak is about two-thirds of what would give unitarity, $12\pi\lambda\!\!\!^{-2}$, for a p-wave resonance. This is fair enough since other processes are present and (5-6) is only an approximation to cross

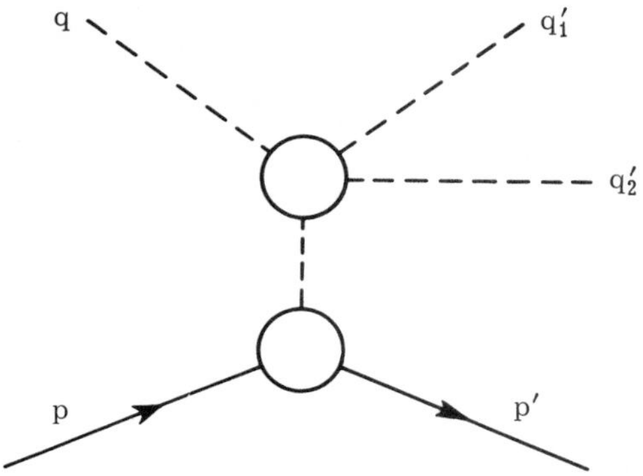

Figure 5-3

section which suffers furthermore from an unknown t-dependence. The width of the peak is of the order of 100 MeV.

$\pi\pi$ interaction then shows a p-wave T = 1 resonance called the "ρ-particle." The branching ratio $\pi^+\pi^- n/\pi^-\pi^0 p$ in $\pi^- + p$ collision is found equal to 2 when the two mesons are produced at the resonance energy. This is what is expected from a T = 1 $\pi\pi$ interaction. The angular distribution in the 2π center-of-mass system shows clearly a $\cos^2\theta$ term for $\pi^-\pi^0$ production.[39] For $\pi^+\pi^-$ production at the same energy it is not so clear and this shows that other amplitudes are present besides the 1π-exchange graph or that the isospin 0 $\pi\pi$ amplitude is also large at the ρ mass.

The 2π decay mode of the ρ-meson is a strong-interaction process. G-parity of the ρ is even. Electromagnetic modes such as $\pi^0\gamma$ must occur but with a very small probability (1 per cent say). A strong decay into $\eta + \pi$ is forbidden.

5–5 THE f_0-MESON

At higher energies (3 to 6 BeV) both the ρ and another peak at 1250 MeV show up on $\pi^+\pi^-$ mass distribution. In charged 2π systems only the ρ appears. This new $\pi\pi$ resonance should then have isotopic spin 0, hence an even spin. It is called the f^0. The angular distribution of the pions in the 2π center-of-mass system is far from uniform with a forward-backward asymmetry passing through zero at the f^0 energy, as expected from a dominating resonance state. This excludes spin 0, and the most likely assignment is spin 2 [a $0(2^{++})$ particle].

In fact, a $\pi\pi$ resonance with such quantum numbers is welcome in the Regge pole formalism.[40] The vacuum trajectory was determined in the physical region ($t < 0$) from the analysis of the shrinking of the diffraction peak in pp scattering. With a slope of the order of

$1/(1\text{ BeV})^2$ assumed to be correct even in the unphysical region for scattering ($t > 0$), one expects a resonance with the quantum numbers of the vacuum, spin and parity 2^+ in the neighborhood of 1 BeV or, at least, a large D-wave $\pi\pi$ phase shift.

The f^0 discovery came at the same time as the π-nucleon diffraction scattering experiments in the 10-20 BeV region[41] which voids any confidence in the slope of the vacuum trajectory as determined from pp scattering.

5–6 THE φ_0-MESON

A resonance in the $K\overline{K}$ system has been found at an energy of 1020 MeV[32] with a small width ($\Gamma < 3$ MeV). It is observed in both reactions $K^-p \to \Lambda + K^+ + K^-$ and $K^-p \to \Lambda + K^0 + \overline{K}^0$. When two neutral K are produced at the resonance energy they always appear as K_1^0 and K_2^0.

$K_1^0 K_2^0$ corresponds to the antisymmetric components of a $K^0 \overline{K}^0$ system. The wave function has then to be odd since the K are bosons and the φ_0 spin is then odd. The φ_0 is then odd under charge conjugation. If its G-parity were even the main decay mode should be into 2π, where nothing comparable to the φ_0 is found in $\pi^+\pi^-$ mass distribution. The G-parity must be odd to forbid this decay, at least for strong processes, and the isotopic spin is then zero as follows from the relation $G = C(-1)^T$ and the conservation of isotopic spin in the production reactions. Spin 1 is much favored, as opposed to spin 3, say, by the $K^+K^-/K^0\overline{K}^0$ branching ratio. Since the Q-value for this decay reaction is very small, centrifugal barrier effects and Coulomb corrections are important enough to differentiate appreciably between the two modes.

The φ_0 has then the same quantum numbers as the ω. It should decay into $\pi^+\pi^-\pi^0$ (most probably $\rho\pi$) with an appreciable probability.

5–7 THE K^*-MESON

The K^* is a resonance in the $K\pi$ system at an energy of 888 MeV[33] with a width of the order of 50 MeV. It is clearly seen in $K^{\pm}p \to K + \pi + N$ reactions and in antiproton annihilation at rest. The charge states in which it is observed imply an isotopic spin $\frac{1}{2}$.

At present the best evidence for its spin comes from the analysis of the $\overline{p}p \to K^0 + \overline{K}^0 + \pi^0$ annihilation at rest, when a K^* is, in fact, observed with the π^0 and either of the K-mesons.

If the annihilation occurs in S state, as it is almost certain to, a spin 0 K^* cannot be obtained in such a reaction from the $^3S_0$ state, as follows from parity and angular momentum conservation. The reaction is possible from the $^1S_0$ state but this state is even under C. One should then observe either $K_1^0 K_1^0 \pi^0$ or $K_2^0 K_2^0 \pi^0$ but not the $K_1^0 K_2^0 \pi^0$

Table 5-1

Spin parity	Strangeness	Isospin G-parity	Name	Mass, MeV	Width, MeV
0^-	0	1^-	π	140	
		0^+	η	550	< 7
	1	$\frac{1}{2}$	K	494	
	−1		$\overline{K}$		
1^-	0	1^+	ρ	750	100
		0^-	ω	780	<10
			φ_0	1020	< 3
	1	$\frac{1}{2}$	K*	885	50
	−1		$\overline{K}$*		
2^+(?)	0	0^+	f_0	1250	100(?)

configuration which is found experimentally.[42] This rules out spin 0. The K* spin is most likely one.

There is some evidence for another $K\pi$ narrow resonance at an energy of 730 MeV.

5–8 A FEW REMARKS

The ρ, ω, and φ_0 mesons are all vector particles and odd under charge conjugation. They should then play an important role in the nucleon form factors. The T = 0, ω and φ, affect the isoscalar form factors and the T = 1, ρ, affects the isovector form factors. In fact, such a $\pi\pi$ resonance was predicted from the dispersion theory analysis of the isovector nucleon form factors[43] long before its discovery in π-nucleon inelastic scattering. The presence of the ρ and the ω and φ_0 at similar energies may help to understand the absence of charge distribution for the neutron, the isoscalar and isovector form factors canceling their effects (see Chapter 7).

Production cross sections for these new mesons in π-nucleon collisions would be interesting to know in order to see if they are related to prominent π-nucleon scattering features. The η and ω (and ρ) thresholds, respectively, coincide with the second and third resonances.

These new particles fit nicely within the eightfold-way scheme of unitary symmetry.[26] The $\pi(S = 0, T = 1)$, $\eta(S = 0, T = 0)$, and $K\overline{K}$ $(S = \pm 1, T = \frac{1}{2})$ makes up an octuplet of pseudoscalar particles. It is even astonishing that the mass formula

$$m_K^2 = \frac{3m_\eta^2}{4} + \frac{m_\pi^2}{4}$$

works so well. The ρ(S = 0, T = 1), ω (S = 0, T = 0), and $K^*\overline{K}^*$ (S = ± 1, T = $\frac{1}{2}$) constitute in a similar way an octuplet of vector particles. The φ_0 would then correspond to a vector, unitary singlet. The observed ω and φ_0 mesons could, however, correspond to a mixing of the two representations.[44]

One can also note that the π, η, ρ, and ω quantum numbers illustrate all the possible nucleon-antinucleon S states; the K and K* quantum numbers, the two nucleon antilambda states.

5–9 OTHER PEAKS

We have discussed so far only the presently well established particles. Many more peaks in mass distributions have been reported but more work is still needed to see if they really correspond to new particles. We shall just discuss one example, the ABC particle.[45]

An anomaly is found in the He^3 spectrum at fixed laboratory angle in the reaction $p + d \rightarrow He^3 + x$, where x stands for a nonobserved two-particle (at least) state. This anomaly shows up as a peak close to the upper limit of the spectrum. No such peak is found in the $p + d \rightarrow He^3 + x$ and this associates the anomaly with a T = 0 state. This could correspond to a new T = 0 meson but lacking other data this can be explained in terms of $\pi\pi$ final-state interaction if the T = 0 S-wave $\pi\pi$ scattering length is large ($2/\mu$, say). This is, however, the only evidence so far for such a large S-wave cross section.

The spectrum anomaly observed in the $K_1^0 K_1^0$ system, close to the threshold, could be of a similar nature.

6

DISPERSION-RELATIONS ANALYSIS OF PION-NUCLEON SCATTERING

6–1 UNITARITY, ANALYTICITY, AND CROSSING SYMMETRY

At present, analysis of strong interactions relies upon five quite general properties of scattering amplitudes. The first two are Lorentz invariance and charge independence. They are used to restrict the reaction amplitudes to a few independent ones. Their consequences have been discussed in detail in the preceding chapters. The other three basic properties that these amplitudes obey are unitarity, crossing symmetry, and some analyticity. Used simultaneously, they provide the present framework for theoretical approach to strong-interaction physics.

In π-nucleon scattering we found that Lorentz invariance and charge independence reduce the number of independent amplitudes down to four functions of the kinematical invariants s, t, and u previously introduced (1-20a, b). We considered the $A^{(\pm)}$ and $B^{(\pm)}$ amplitudes. For the sake of simplicity let us first neglect spin and charge. There would be one single amplitude M(s,t,u). If we further consider forward scattering the momentum transfer is fixed (t = 0) and the amplitude is a function of s only or equivalently of $u = 2(m^2 + \mu^2) - s$ (1-20). It is, in fact, either conjectured, or shown to follow from the axioms of field theory, to be the boundary value of an analytic function of s, when s has a positive, infinitesimal, imaginary part.

In quantum field theory, for instance, the amplitude may be expressed as the Fourier transform of the matrix element between an initial and a final one-nucleon state, of a retarded commutator of π-meson field operators. When causality is imposed in assuming that this commutator has to vanish outside the light cone, the scattering amplitude is found to be an analytic function of s in the complex s-plane with the following singularities:[1,2] two cuts along the real axis from $-\infty$ to $(m - \mu)^2$ and from $(m + \mu)^2$ to $+\infty$; and two poles at $s = m^2$ and $s = m^2 + 2\mu^2$.

For physical values of s, $s \geq (m + \mu)^2$, the imaginary part of M is simply given by the unitarity relation (1-25). The imaginary part gets contributions from all possible intermediate states. For $(m + \mu)^2 \leq s < (m + 2\mu)^2$ we have only to consider π-nucleon states [both matrix elements in (1-24) would refer to π-nucleon elastic scattering]. For $(m + 2\mu)^2 < s < (m + 3\mu)^2$ we also have to consider 2π-nucleon states. One pion production, matrix elements have also to be introduced in the unitarity relation. For higher value of s, intermediate states with more particles, accessible with conservation of charge, baryonic number, and total isotopic spin, have to be considered. It follows that M(s) must have a branch point singularity at each threshold. The simplest definition of M, consistent with unitarity, implies a cut along the real positive axis extending from $(m + \mu)^2$ to $+\infty$.

Now, crossing symmetry implies that the same amplitude, considered as an analytic function of s, also describes π-nucleon scattering in the reaction obtained by crossing. As explained in Chapter 1, we exchange here the role of s and u, keeping t fixed. The physical region for this new reaction is defined by $u \geq (m + \mu)^2$, $t = 0$. From unitarity alone we have, therefore, to consider as well a cut in the u-plane, for real u extending from $(m + \mu)^2$ to $+\infty$.

As an analytic function of s, M(s) has therefore at least two cuts on the real axis: a cut from $(m + \mu)^2$ to $+\infty$ (unitarity in the direct reaction) and a cut from $-\infty$ to $(m - \mu)^2$ (unitarity in the crossed reaction).

For $(m - \mu)^2 < s < (m + \mu)^2$ the scattering amplitude is real. M(s) is then a "real" analytic function‡ and the discontinuity across the cuts is simply given by twice its imaginary part, namely

$$M(s + i\epsilon) - M(s - i\epsilon) = 2i \operatorname{Im} M(s + i\epsilon) \tag{6-1}$$

We have so far avoided mentioning one particular intermediate state, which is the one-nucleon state. The transition $\pi + N \rightarrow N$ is not a physical process, and the one-nucleon state does not appear in the unitarity relation written in (1-24). Nevertheless, the nucleon has the same quantum numbers as a π-nucleon system and when one investigates the analytic property of the scattering amplitude in the framework of quantum field theory one finds that it does contribute. It gives a pole in the scattering amplitude for an unphysical value of s, $s = m^2$. Similarly we also have a pole at $u = m^2$. In the complex s-plane this gives, respectively, two poles at $s = m^2$ and $s = m^2 + 2\mu^2$. These poles are found in perturbation theory. They correspond to

---

‡Namely, $M^*(s^*) = M(s)$.

the Born approximation terms. The residue of the poles is simply related to the squared renormalized π-nucleon coupling constant g^2.

The singularities of the forward scattering amplitude, which have been thus presented on an intuitive basis are precisely the ones encountered in quantum field theory, when microcausality is assumed.

One may as well assume, as a working hypothesis, that they are, indeed, the only singularities.

Instead of s we consider a slightly more convenient variable $\nu = (s - m^2 - \mu^2)/2m$. If $q_1 p_1$ (and $p_2 p_2$) stand for the pion and nucleon momenta in the initial (and final) states, $\nu = p_i q_i/m$. ν is the incident π-meson energy in the laboratory. In the complex ν-plane we have poles at $\nu = \mp\mu^2/2m$ and two cuts on the real axis extending from $-\infty$ to $-\mu$ and from μ to $+\infty$ (Fig. 6-1).

We can then write the forward scattering amplitude for any value of ν in terms of a Cauchy integral. An integral along contour C of Fig. 6-1 does not enclose any singularity.

$$
\begin{aligned}
2\pi i M(\nu) &= \oint_C \frac{M(\nu')\,d\nu'}{\nu' - \nu} \\
&= \int_{-\infty}^{-\mu} \frac{M(\nu' + i\epsilon) - M(\nu' - i\epsilon)}{\nu' - \nu}\, d\nu' \\
&\quad + \int_{\mu}^{\infty} \frac{M(\nu' + i\epsilon) - M(\nu' - i\epsilon)}{\nu' - \nu}\, d\nu' \\
&\quad - 2\pi i \left(\frac{\Gamma}{-(\mu^2/2m) - \nu} + \frac{\Gamma'}{(\mu^2/2m) - \nu} \right) \\
&\quad + \oint_{C'} \frac{M(\nu')\,d\nu'}{\nu' - \nu}
\end{aligned}
\tag{6-2}
$$

Γ and Γ' are the residues of the scattering amplitude at $\nu = -\mu^2/2m$ and $\nu = \mu^2/2m$. They are opposite from crossing symmetry (6-6).

The contour C′ represents the two half-circles at infinity. The decomposition just written makes sense only if $M(\nu)$ goes to zero

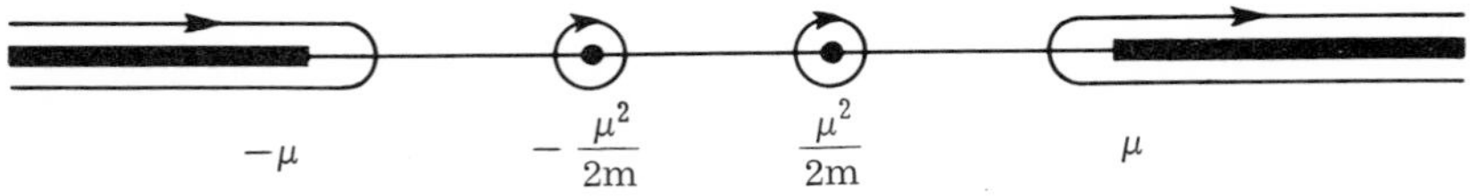

Figure 6-1
The ν-plane.

when $|\nu|$ goes to infinity.‡ We first suppose that this is indeed the case. We may then neglect the contribution of the contour integral along C′. Together with (6-1) we get

$$M(\nu) = \Gamma\left(\frac{1}{(\mu^2/2m) + \nu} + \frac{1}{(\mu^2/2m) - \nu}\right) + \frac{1}{\pi}\int_{-\infty}^{-\mu} \frac{\operatorname{Im} M(\nu')\, d\nu'}{\nu' - \nu} + \frac{1}{\pi}\int_{\mu}^{\infty} \frac{\operatorname{Im} M(\nu')\, d\nu'}{\nu' - \nu} \tag{6-3}$$

6–2 DISPERSION RELATIONS

The physical amplitude (ν real $\geq \mu$) is defined as the boundary value of M when the positive real axis is approached from above

$$M(\nu) = \lim_{\eta \to 0} \left\{\frac{\Gamma}{(\mu^2/2m) + \nu} + \frac{\Gamma}{(\mu^2/2m) - \nu} + \frac{1}{\pi}\int_{-\infty}^{-\mu} \frac{\operatorname{Im} M(\nu')\, d\nu'}{\nu' - \nu} + \frac{1}{\pi}\int_{\mu}^{\infty} \frac{\operatorname{Im} M(\nu')}{\nu' - \nu - i\eta}\, d\nu'\right\}$$

Taking the real parts of both sides we obtain the relation

$$\operatorname{Re} M(\nu) = \Gamma\left(\frac{1}{(\mu^2/2m) + \nu} + \frac{1}{(\mu^2/2m) - \nu}\right) + \frac{1}{\pi}\int_{-\infty}^{-\mu} \frac{\operatorname{Im} M(\nu')\, d\nu'}{\nu' - \nu} + \frac{1}{\pi} P\int_{\mu}^{\infty} \frac{\operatorname{Im} M(\nu')\, d\nu'}{\nu' - \nu} \tag{6-4}$$

‡We will assume that $M(\nu) \sim \nu^{-\alpha}$ when $|\nu| \to \infty$, where α is any positive number.

This is known as a dispersion relation.‡ The symbol P in front of the integral means that we have to take only its principal value

$$\frac{1}{\nu' - \nu - i\eta} \rightarrow P\,\frac{1}{\nu' - \nu} + i\pi\,\delta(\nu' - \nu)$$

For $\nu \geq \mu$, Im $M(\nu)$ is the imaginary part of the physical forward scattering amplitude. It is simply related to the total cross section. Namely,

$$\text{Im } M(\nu) = 2m\sqrt{\nu^2 - \mu^2}\;\sigma_{tot}(\nu) \tag{6-5}$$

This is the optical theorem (1-25), since qW can be written as $m\sqrt{\nu^2 - \mu^2}$.

To use (6-4) we also need the imaginary part of the forward scattering amplitude for $\nu < -\mu$, hence for nonphysical values of s. However this corresponds to physical values of μ in the reaction obtained through crossing, and we can use crossing symmetry. With neutral and spinless particles this is done in the following way. The scattering amplitude—strictly speaking its real part since the imaginary part of the amplitude is not unambiguously defined in an unphysical region—does not change when we exchange s and u or, as is easily seen, when we change the sign of ν. Namely,

$$\text{Re } M(-\nu) = \text{Re } M(\nu) \tag{6-6}$$

As shown in Chapter 3 this is intuitive from perturbation theory. It can be proved in quantum field theory but one may as well consider it as a working hypothesis. M is the amplitude with sufficient analytic property so that the analytic continuation between the two physical regions is defined without ambiguity. From (6-4) and (6-6) one gets

$$\text{Im } M(-\nu) = -\text{Im } M(\nu) \tag{6-7}$$

In other words, the limit obtained when the u-real-positive axis is approached with a positive imaginary part is equal to the limit obtained when the corresponding value of the s-real-negative axis is approached with a negative imaginary part. We have $s + t + u = 2(m^2 + \mu^2)$. (6-4) is then brought to the following form:

$$\text{Re } M(\nu) = +\Gamma\left(\frac{1}{(\mu^2/2m) + \nu} + \frac{1}{(\mu^2/2m) - \nu}\right)$$

$$+ \frac{1}{\pi}\,P\int_{\mu}^{\infty} \text{Im } M(\nu')\,d\nu'\left(\frac{1}{\nu' - \nu} + \frac{1}{\nu' + \nu}\right) \tag{6-8}$$

‡For a discussion of dispersion relation in classical physics see Refs. 1 and 2.

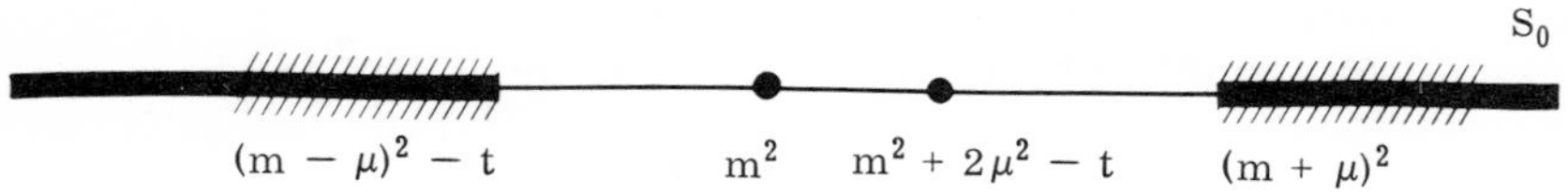

Figure 6-2
The s-plane. The hatched part of the cut indicates the region where the discontinuity has to be obtained through extrapolation to $|\cos\theta| > 1$. S_0 is the threshold for scattering.

Together with (6-5) this provides a relation among experimental quantities only, with one parameter Γ.

Such a dispersion relation for π-nucleon forward scattering has been, in fact, proved, in the framework of field theory. One may write a similar relation, at fixed momentum transfer, assuming as a working hypothesis, that the same kinds of singularities only are present. If we fix t at a particular negative value, the physical values of s correspond to $q^2 \geq -4t$, where q is the center-of-mass momentum. It is calculated from s by the relation

$$q^2 = \frac{s^2 - 2s(m^2+\mu^2) + (m^2-\mu^2)^2}{4s}$$

As we had to take the one-nucleon intermediate state it is now necessary to include all π-nucleon intermediate states even if they correspond to an unphysical value of the center-of-mass momentum $0 \leq q^2 \leq -4t$. The cut in s extends from $(m+\mu)^2$ to $+\infty$ as for forward scattering. The cut in u also from $(m+\mu)^2$ to $+\infty$. The singularities in the s-plane at fixed t are shown on Fig. 6-2. The relation (6-8) is generalized as follows:

$$\begin{aligned}\operatorname{Re} M(s,t) &= -2m\Gamma\left(\frac{1}{m^2-s} + \frac{1}{s-m^2-2\mu^2+t}\right)\\ &\quad + \frac{1}{\pi}\int_{(m+\mu)^2}^{\infty} \operatorname{Im} M(s',t)\, ds'\\ &\quad \times\left(\frac{1}{s'-s} + \frac{1}{s'+s-2m^2-2\mu^2+t}\right) \qquad (6\text{-}9)\end{aligned}$$

Such a dispersion relation, for fixed momentum transfer π-nucleon scattering, has also been proved to be valid in field theory, provided that[46]

$$0 < -t < \tfrac{32}{3}\mu^2\,\frac{2m+\mu}{2m-\mu}$$

It is at present conjectured to be valid for all values of t. No contradiction has been found and conclusions are in agreement with experiments. These dispersion relations are not so simple to use as the forward scattering dispersion relations, since the imaginary part of the scattering amplitude is no longer obtained from the optical theorem. Furthermore its value between $s = (m + \mu)^2$ and the limit of the physical region $q^2 = -4t$ is not a physical quantity. It has to be computed through analytic continuation from the physical region.[46]

6–3 PHENOMENOLOGICAL APPLICATIONS OF DISPERSION RELATIONS

To use the following dispersion relations for the analysis of π-nucleon scattering we have first to face the so-called unessential complications due to spin and charge. Such complications are considered as unessential since all four amplitudes $A^{(\pm)}$ and $B^{(\pm)}$ enjoy the same analytic properties. They have been, in fact, selected for this purpose. Considering spin and charge does not require any new dynamical property to be introduced. It merely complicates the algebra.

We first consider the forward dispersion relation.[47] The forward scattering amplitude reads [(1-16) and (3-15)]

$$-2m\bar{u}(p)\left[\left(-A^{(+)} + i\frac{B^{(\pm)}}{2}\gamma(q_1 + q_2)\right)\delta_{\alpha\beta} + \tfrac{1}{2}[\tau_\beta, \tau_\alpha]\left(-A^{(-)} + i\frac{B^{(-)}}{2}\gamma(q_1 + q_2)\right)\right]u(p)$$

Written as an operator in the nucleon charge space

$$F^{(+)}\delta_{\alpha\beta} + F^{(-)}\tfrac{1}{2}[\tau_\alpha, \tau_\beta]$$

it reduces to

$$F^{(\pm)} = 2m(A^{(\pm)} + \nu B^{(\pm)})$$

This simplification comes from the fact that the spin-flip amplitude vanishes in the forward direction. We already wrote the crossing relations. They are (3-17)

$$\operatorname{Re} F^{(\pm)}(-\nu) = \pm \operatorname{Re} F^{(\pm)}(\nu)$$

or

$$\operatorname{Re} A^{(\pm)}(-\nu) = \pm \operatorname{Re} A^{(\pm)}(\nu)$$
$$\operatorname{Re} B^{(\pm)}(-\nu) = \mp \operatorname{Re} B^{(\pm)}(\nu) \qquad (6\text{-}10)$$

We now consider in more detail the contribution of the one-nucleon state to the dispersion integral. The amplitude $\pi + N \rightarrow N$ is just a number, since all vertex quantities are fixed by the conservation of energy and momentum. Its contribution to the imaginary part of the forward scattering amplitude is then written in the following way (we first neglect charge):

$$\pi g^2 \frac{\mu^2}{2m}\left[\delta\left(\nu - \frac{\mu^2}{2m}\right) - \delta\left(\nu + \frac{\mu^2}{2m}\right)\right] \qquad (6\text{-}11)$$

This gives the two pole terms in the scattering amplitude at $\nu = \pm\mu^2/2m$, which is the energy at which a π-nucleon state can go into a single nucleon state with conservation of energy and momentum. This is an unphysical energy but through the dispersion relation (6-8) these poles contribute to the physical scattering amplitude at all energies.

In field theory the contribution to the imaginary part of the forward amplitude due to the single nucleon state reads (Born terms)

$$m(2\pi)^4 \,|\, G((p - p_i)^2) \,|^2 \sum \{\bar{u}(p_i)\gamma_5 \tau_\alpha u(p)\bar{u}(p)\gamma_5 \tau_\beta$$
$$\times\, u(p_i)\ \delta(k + p - p_i) - \bar{u}(p_i)\gamma_5 \tau_\beta u(p)\bar{u}(p)\gamma_5 \tau_\alpha$$
$$\times\, u(p_i)\ \delta(k + p_i - p)\} \qquad (6\text{-}12)$$

The second term is simply obtained from (1-24) in extending formally the unitarity relation to the one-nucleon intermediate state. The first one corresponds to the reaction obtained through crossing of the initial and final pions. α (and β) is the intial (and final) meson charge index ($\alpha = 1,2,3$); k is the intial meson momentum; and Σ stands for a summation over all intermediate one-nucleon states (momentum and spin). G is a function of the only independent invariant we have when both nucleons are on the mass shell ($p^2 = p_i^2 = -m^2$). $G(-\mu^2)$ defines the π-nucleon renormalized coupling constant.[48] It is the only value to appear in the dispersion relation.

The summation over the intermediate state (momenta and spins) required in (6-12) is readily obtained. We write it in terms of the ν variable. This gives‡

‡One may as well calculate directly the contribution of the Born approximation terms.

$$\pi g^2 \nu_B \{\delta_{\beta\alpha} (\delta(\nu - \nu_B) - \delta(\nu + \nu_B)) + \tfrac{1}{2}[\tau_\beta, \tau_\alpha] (\delta(\nu - \nu_B) + \delta(\nu + \nu_B))\} \tag{6-13}$$

with

$$\nu_B = -\frac{\mu^2}{2m} \tag{6-14}$$

This is (6-11) when charge has been taken into account. The first term belongs to $F^{(+)}$; the second one belongs to $F^{(-)}$.

We rewrite (6-4)

$$\operatorname{Re} F^{(\pm)}(\nu) = -g^2 \frac{\mu^2}{2m}\left(\frac{1}{\nu_B - \nu} \pm \frac{1}{\nu_B + \nu}\right) + \frac{1}{\pi}\int_{-\infty}^{-\mu} \frac{\operatorname{Im} F^{(\pm)}(\nu')}{\nu' - \nu}\, d\nu' + \frac{1}{\pi} P \int_{\mu}^{\infty} \frac{\operatorname{Im} F^{(\pm)}(\nu')}{\nu' - \nu}\, d\nu'$$

(6-10) and (6-4) imply

$$\operatorname{Im} F^{(\pm)}(-\nu) = \mp \operatorname{Im} F^{(\pm)}(\nu)$$

We obtain

$$\operatorname{Re} F^{(\pm)}(\nu) = -g^2 \frac{\mu^2}{2m}\left(\frac{1}{\nu_B - \nu} \pm \frac{1}{\nu_B + \nu}\right) + \frac{1}{\pi} P \int_{\mu}^{\infty} \operatorname{Im} F^{(\pm)}(\nu') \times d\nu'\left(\frac{1}{\nu' - \nu} \pm \frac{1}{\nu' + \nu}\right) \tag{6-15}$$

As mentioned in Chapter 1, $F^{(\pm)} 1/8\pi m$ are the forward scattering amplitudes in the nucleon rest frame: $\mathfrak{F}^{(\pm)}$. In terms of these amplitudes, (6-15) reads

$$\text{Re } \mathfrak{F}^{(+)}(\nu) = 2\left(\frac{f^2}{4\pi} \frac{-\nu_B}{\nu_B^2 - \nu^2} + \frac{1}{\pi} P \int_{\mu}^{\infty} \frac{\text{Im } \mathfrak{F}^{(+)}(\nu')\nu' \, d\nu'}{(\nu'^2 - \nu^2)}\right)$$

$$\text{Re } \mathfrak{F}^{(-)}(\nu) = 2\nu\left(\frac{f^2}{4\pi} \frac{-1}{\nu_B^2 - \nu^2} + \frac{1}{\pi} P \int_{\mu}^{\infty} \frac{\text{Im } \mathfrak{F}^{(-)}(\nu') \, d\nu'}{(\nu'^2 - \nu^2)}\right) \tag{6-16}$$

where $f^2 = g^2(\mu^2/4m^2)$ is the rationalized renormalized coupling constant introduced in the static theory of π-nucleon interaction.[11] The integrand is given by the optical theorem. We use (3-16) to relate $\mathfrak{F}^{(\pm)}$ to π^+p and π^-p scattering amplitudes. (6-5) gives

$$\text{Im } \mathfrak{F}^{(\pm)}(\nu) = \frac{1}{8\pi} \sqrt{\nu^2 - \mu^2} \, (\sigma_-(\nu) \pm \sigma_+(\nu))$$

where $\sigma_\pm(\nu)$ is the total cross section for $\pi^\pm p$ scattering for an incident meson of laboratory energy ν.

The π^+p and π^-p total cross sections seem to tend toward a common limit with increasing energy (Fig. 6-3). If this is the actual asymptotic behavior and if the cross sections tend toward their limit as $s^{-\alpha}$, where α is any positive number, the second dispersion relation (6-16) makes sense as it stands. We have

$$\frac{\nu^2 - \nu_B^2}{2\nu} \text{Re } \mathfrak{F}^{(-)}(\nu) = \frac{f^2}{4\pi} + \frac{\nu^2 - \nu_B^2}{8\pi^2} P \int_{\mu}^{\infty} \frac{\sqrt{\nu'^2 - \mu^2} \, (\sigma_-(\nu') - \sigma_+(\nu'))}{\nu'^2 - \nu^2} \, d\nu'$$

It is convenient to split the integral into two terms. We write, following Haber-Schaim,[49]

$$\frac{\nu^2 - \nu_B^2}{4\nu}\left(\text{Re } \mathfrak{F}\pi^-p(\nu) - \text{Re } \mathfrak{F}\pi^+p(\nu) - \frac{\nu^3}{2\pi^2} P \int_{\mu}^{\infty} \frac{\sqrt{\nu'^2 - \mu^2} \, (\sigma_-(\nu') - \sigma_+(\nu'))}{\nu'^2(\nu'^2 - \nu^2)} \, d\nu'\right)$$

$$= \frac{f^2}{4\pi} + (\nu^2 - \nu_B^2)\lambda \tag{6-17}$$

where

$$\lambda = \frac{1}{8\pi^2} \, P \int_{\mu}^{\infty} \frac{\sqrt{\nu^2 - \mu^2} \, (\sigma_-(\nu) - \sigma_+(\nu))}{\nu^2} \, d\nu$$

is a constant term.

The left-hand side can be calculated from experimental data. For low value of ν, it should depend only weakly on the high-energy behavior of the cross section. The real part of the scattering amplitude is obtained from the low-energy phase shifts. There is a $\sqrt{\nu^2 - \mu^2}/q$ factor to go from the center-of-mass to the nucleon rest frame amplitudes. If the dispersion relations is correct the left-hand side should be a linear function of ν^2. This is, indeed, found to be the case.

Furthermore, if this linear fit is extrapolated down to $\nu^2 = \nu_B^2 = (\mu^2/2m)^2$ (the experimental points correspond to $\nu \geq \mu$). The second term of the right-hand side does not contribute. The extrapolated value gives the π-nucleon coupling constant. The value, thus obtained,[49] is $f^2/4\pi = 0.08 \pm 0.01$ ($g^2/4\pi = 14$).

This is the first example of the now widely used polology technique. The contribution of a particular process (a one-particle intermediate state) may be isolated and obtained through an extrapolation of physical data to what would result from a negative, kinetic energy, incident particle.

6–4 USE OF SUBTRACTED DISPERSION RELATIONS

If the π^+p and π^-p cross sections tend toward fixed values at high energies, the first relation in (6-16) does not make sense since the integral diverges. Nevertheless $F^{(+)}(\nu)/\nu$ has the same analytic properties as $F^{(+)}(\nu)$ except for a pole at $\nu = 0$. If $F(\nu)$ tends to a constant as $|\nu| \to \infty$, a Cauchy formula, written for $F(\nu)/\nu$, will have the same form as (6-15) with, in addition, the scattering amplitude at $\nu = 0$ (the residue of the additional pole). Namely,

$$\mathrm{Re}\, F^{(+)}(\nu) - \mathrm{Re}\, F^{(+)}(0) = 2\left(\frac{f^2}{4\pi} \, \frac{\nu^2}{(\nu_B^2 - \nu^2)} \right.$$

$$\left. + \frac{\nu^2}{\pi} \, P \int_{\mu}^{\infty} \frac{\mathrm{Im}\, F^{(+)}(\nu')\, d\nu'}{(\nu'^2 - \nu^2)\, \nu'} \right)$$

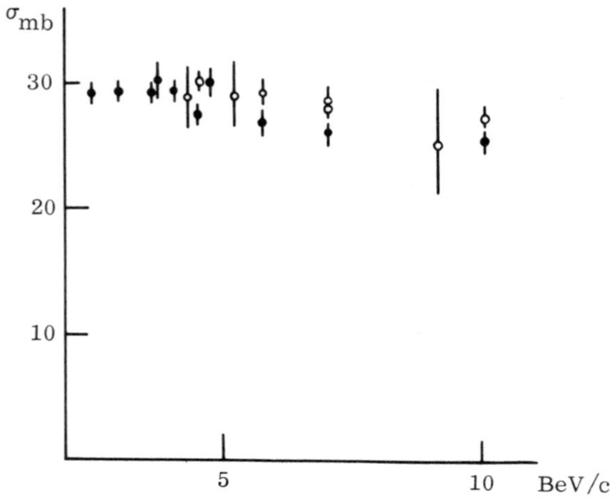

Figure 6-3

This is what we would have obtained in subtracting formally Re $F^{(+)}(0)$ from Re $F^{(+)}(\nu)$, both given by (6-15). This operation is called a "subtraction."

As applied to experimental data such a relation depends in a weaker way on the high-energy behavior of the amplitude. It introduces, however, an extra parameter. If the scattering amplitude behaves like a polynomial in s as $s \to \infty$, s^n, a dispersion relation, will require $n + 1$ such abstractions.

In Fig. 6-3 the π^+p and π^-p total cross section are given as functions of the pion momentum in BeV/c. White (and black) dots represent π^+ (and π^-) data. The cross section is given in millibarns.

For $\mathfrak{F}^{(+)}$ we shall, in fact, do two subtractions at $\nu = \pm\mu$, respectively. The residues at these two points are opposite, as follows from crossing symmetry. We use the optical theorem and obtain

$$\mathrm{Re}\left\{\mathfrak{F}^{(+)}(\nu) - \mathfrak{F}^{(+)}(\mu)\right\}$$

$$= \frac{f^2}{4\pi}\,\frac{\mu^2}{m}\,\frac{\nu^2 - \mu^2}{(\mu^2 - \nu_B^2)(\nu^2 - \nu_B^2)} + \frac{\nu^2 - \mu^2}{4\pi^2}$$

$$\times\ P\int_{\mu}^{\infty} \frac{\nu'(\sigma_+(\nu') + \sigma_-(\nu'))\,d\nu'}{\sqrt{\nu'^2 - \mu^2}\,(\nu'^2 - \nu^2)} \qquad (6\text{-}18)$$

(6-17) and (6-18) may be combined to give dispersion relations for each charge configuration. The agreement with experiment is fine.[50]

Let us assume that σ_+ and σ_- both tend toward a limit as $s \to \infty$, $\sigma(\infty)$. If the limits are not identical, the dispersion relation obtained for $\mathfrak{F}^{(-)}(\nu)$ requires a subtraction to be meaningful. The asymptotic behavior of the real part of the charge-exchange scattering amplitude is then written

$$\operatorname{Re} \mathfrak{F}^-(\nu) \sim c\nu + \frac{\nu^3}{4\pi^2} \times P \int_\mu^\infty \frac{\sqrt{\nu'^2 - \mu^2}\,(\sigma_-(\nu') - \sigma_+(\nu'))\,d\nu'}{\nu'^2(\nu' + \nu)(\nu' - \nu)}$$

where c is a constant. This relation is obtained with two subtractions at $\nu = 0$.

Under reasonable assumptions for the high-energy behavior of the total cross section, the last term behaves asymptotically as:

$$(\sigma_-(\infty) - \sigma_+(\infty))\,\nu \log \nu$$

On the other hand, the asymptotic behavior of the imaginary part of the charge-exchange forward scattering amplitude, as given by the optical theorem, is

$$\operatorname{Im} \mathfrak{F}^{(-)}(\nu) \sim \nu(\sigma_-(\nu) - \sigma_+(\nu))$$

Now, at high energies, interactions are likely to be dominated by inelastic effects. There are so many channels available that there is an almost zero probability to find again the initial state once two particles interact. The inelasticity parameters for all partial waves go to zero and the scattering amplitudes become pure imaginary. One then expects the ratio $\operatorname{Re} \mathfrak{F}^{(-)}/\operatorname{Im} \mathfrak{F}^{(-)}$ to go to zero as $\nu \to \infty$, or at least to be bounded.

Together with the results obtained from the forward dispersion relation when both cross sections tend toward constants this is possible only if both σ_+ and σ_- tend toward the same limit. One can then calculate c and verify that this condition is sufficient. This is the Pomeranchuck theorem.[51]

If all inelasticity parameters go to zero, there is pure absorption and shadow scattering. The center-of-mass elastic scattering amplitudes have the same limit for all partial waves, namely, $i/\sqrt{S}$ (4-3). This results in a strong forward peak. This is quite similar to the diffraction of light obtained with an array of identical particles having a large radius with respect to the wavelength. By analogy it is called "diffraction peak."

Let us note, however, that a pure imaginary, forward scattering amplitude does not imply imaginary partial-wave amplitudes or pure shadow scattering.

6–5 FIXED MOMENTUM TRANSFER AND SPIN-FLIP DISPERSION RELATIONS

For nonforward scattering we have to write separate dispersion relations for $A^{(\pm)}$ and $B^{(\pm)}$. One checks that the nucleon pole terms appear only in $B^{(\pm)}$. Taking proper care of spin and charge, as done previously for forward scattering, one writes relations similar to (6-9)

$$\operatorname{Re} A^{(\pm)}(s,t) = \frac{1}{\pi} P \int_{(m+\mu)^2}^{\infty} ds' \operatorname{Im} A^{(\pm)}(s',t) \times \left(\frac{1}{s'-s} \pm \frac{1}{s'+s-2m^2-2\mu^2+t} \right)$$

$$\operatorname{Re} B^{(\pm)}(s,t) = \frac{g^2}{m^2-s} \mp \frac{1}{s-m^2-2\mu^2-t} + \frac{1}{\pi} P \int_{(m+\mu)^2}^{\infty} ds' \operatorname{Im} B^{(\pm)}(s',t) \times \left(\frac{1}{s'-s} \mp \frac{1}{s'+s-2m^2-2\mu^2+t} \right) \tag{6-19}$$

Chew, Low, Goldeberger, and Nambu[3] have discussed in detail the application of such dispersion relations. They obtain equations for the partial-wave amplitudes.

In order to do so, one has to express $A^{(\pm)}(s,t)$ and $B^{(\pm)}(s,t)$ in terms of the $f^{T}_{\ell\pm}$ amplitudes using (1-19), (1-23), and (2-24). The scattering amplitudes for unphysical values of t that are required for $0 \le q^2 \le -4t$ may be obtained through analytic continuation of the Legendre polynomials for each partial-wave amplitude. This is possible as long as the partial-wave expansion converges.[46] The expressions obtained are extremely complicated but they simplify highly when only the $j = \frac{3}{2}$, $T = \frac{3}{2}$ resonance is retained in the dispersion integrals and when low-energy approximations are made. The important result of this approach in the derivation of an effective range formula for the $j = T = \frac{3}{2}$, p-wave phase shift which reads

$$q^3 \cot \delta^{3/2}_{13/2} = \omega \frac{4}{3} \left(\frac{\mu}{2m}\right)^2 \frac{g^2}{4\pi} (1 - r\omega) \tag{6-20}$$

where q and ω are the center-of-mass momentum and energy of the π-meson,‡ and r is a parameter. This formula gives a good fit to the experimental data and provides a further method to obtain g^2. Pion photoproduction may be discussed in a similar way.[52]

To conclude, we briefly discuss spin-flip dispersion relations.[53] We have written down a dispersion relation for $B^{(\pm)}(s,t)$. Now, as shown by (1-19) as long as the nucleon center-of-mass energy is not too large as compared to this mass, B depends weakly on f_1, and highly on f_2, and vice versa. Hence a dispersion relation for B at $t = 0$ is called a "spin-flip dispersion relation." We consider the second dispersion relation in (6-19) for $t = 0$ and subtract $B^{(-)}$ from $B^{(+)}$ to get the isotopic spin $\frac{3}{2}$ spin-flip amplitude (3-16),

$$\begin{aligned} \mathrm{Re}\, B^{3/2}(s,0) = & -\frac{2g^2}{s - m^2 - 2\mu^2} \\ & + \frac{1}{\pi} P \int_{(m+\mu)^2}^{\infty} ds' \frac{\mathrm{Im}\, B^{3/2}(s',0)}{s' - s} \\ & - \frac{1}{\pi} \int_{(m+\mu)^2}^{\infty} ds' \frac{\mathrm{Im}\, B^{3/2}(s',0) + 2\, \mathrm{Im}\, B^{1/2}(s',0)}{3(s' + s - 2(m^2 + \mu^2))} \end{aligned} \tag{6-21}$$

The contribution from isotopic spin $\frac{1}{2}$, which is unimportant up to 200 MeV, appears in the nonsingular integral only. It can, therefore, be neglected. (6-21) is put in a more convenient form as follows:

$$\begin{aligned} m\left(\nu - \frac{\mu^2}{2m}\right)\Bigg[-\mathrm{Re}\, B^{3/2}(\nu) + \frac{2}{3}\,\frac{\nu}{\pi} & \\ \times P \int_{\mu}^{\infty} d\nu' \frac{(2\nu' + \nu)}{\nu'(\nu'^2 - \nu^2)}\ \mathrm{Im}\, B^{3/2}(\nu')\Bigg] & \\ = g^2 - m\left(\nu - \frac{\mu^2}{2m}\right)\frac{2}{3\pi} & \\ \times \int_{\mu}^{\infty} \frac{\mathrm{Im}\, B^{3/2}(\nu')\, d\nu'}{\nu'} & \end{aligned} \tag{6-22}$$

As before, we have introduced the variable $\nu = (s - m^2 - \mu^2)/2m$.

‡In fact, $\omega = W - m$.

The relation obtained is in a form similar to (6-17). The left-hand side can be calculated from the isotopic spin $\frac{3}{2}$ phase shifts.

One has to verify a linear dependence on ν of the left-hand side, as determined from the data. We get the value of g^2 with an extrapolation to $\nu = \mu^2/2m$. This is satisfied by the Fermi set of phase shifts but not by the Yang set.[53] The spin-flip dispersion relation provides the answer to a question that could have been settled, on a pure phenomenological basis, only by a different polarization measurement.

7

NEARBY SINGULARITIES AND PERIPHERAL MODEL

7–1 NEARBY SINGULARITIES

In the preceding chapter we have shown how analyticity properties of the fixed, momentum transfer, amplitude could be used to obtain powerful relations for the analysis of π-nucleon scattering. Let us write the dispersion relation (6-19) in the following unsubtracted form:

$$\begin{aligned} \operatorname{Re} B(s,t) &= \frac{g^2}{m^2 - s} + \frac{g^2}{m^2 - u} \\ &+ \frac{1}{\pi} \int_{(m+\mu)^2}^{\infty} \frac{B_s(s',t)}{s' - s}\, ds' \\ &+ \frac{1}{\pi} \int_{(m+\mu)^2}^{\infty} \frac{B_u(u',t)}{u' - u}\, du' \end{aligned} \tag{7-1}$$

For physical values of s, ($q_s^2 \geq -4t$), $B_s(s,t)$ is the imaginary part of the scattering amplitude. In a similar way, it is easy to check that $B_u(u,t)$ is the imaginary part of the scattering amplitude of the reaction obtained through crossing, for physical values of $u > (m + \mu)^2$. B_s and B_u are called the "fixed t, absorptive parts of the scattering amplitude." So far we have used analyticity in s for fixed t but one can go further and assume that the absorptive parts also satisfy dispersion relations in t.‡ Mandelstam considered this possibility[4]

‡They are obviously not analytic functions of s (and u).

and was led to conjecture analyticity properties in the two variables. Full crossing symmetry is used. As an analytic function of both s and t, B(s,t) describes π-nucleon scattering but also the $\pi\pi \to$ NN reaction, the physical region of which corresponds to $t \geq 4m^2$, $s,u \leq 0$ (Fig. 1-4).

Singularities in all variables are assumed to result from unitarity in all three channels. They are confined to the s, t, and u positive real axis. The asymptotic behavior of the amplitude is assumed to be at most polynomial in all three variables. These properties lead to the Mandelstam representation for the scattering amplitude.

To discuss any of its implications would be outside the scope of these notes. We shall merely discuss the particular importance of nearby singularities, the existence of which can be guessed from perturbation theory.

In the preceding chapter we considered the singularities of the π-nucleon scattering amplitudes, in the s (and u) variables, and we emphasized the important role of the nucleon pole. When the scattering amplitude is considered as an analytic function of both s and t (and u) we expect to have a pole of the amplitude whenever there exists a particle with the same quantum number as the two initial (or final) particles in any of the three reactions described by the same kinematical invariants s, t, and u.

In order to illustrate this let us consider nucleon-nucleon scattering, neglecting charge and spin. Particles 1 and 2 are ingoing, particles 3 and 4 are outgoing (Fig. 7-1). There is only one invariant amplitude A(s,t,u) which, considered as an analytic function of the three complex variables, describes six different reactions obtained when any two of the four particles involved are considered as ingoing, the other two being outgoing. The NN (1 and 2 ingoing) and the $N\overline{N}$ (1 and 3 or 1 and 4 ingoing) scattering amplitudes all are different boundary values of A. There exists one particle with the same quantum numbers as the two-nucleon system: the deuteron. We have then a pole in A for an unphysical value of s: $s = m_d^2$.

Now the $N\overline{N}$ system has the same quantum number as a π-meson. A has then a pole in t and a pole in u, and we write

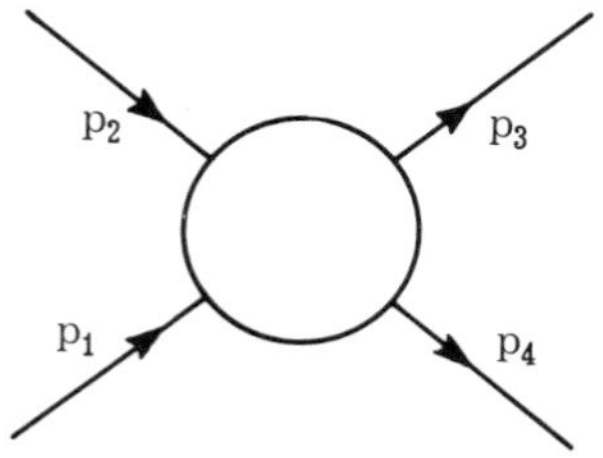

Figure 7-1

$$A(s,t,u) = \Gamma\left(\frac{1}{t - \mu^2} + \frac{1}{u - \mu^2}\right) + A'(s,t,u) \qquad (7\text{-}2)$$

where $A'(s,t,u)$ is regular at $t = \mu^2$ and $u = \mu^2$.

The one-pion state is the lowest mass state with the $N\bar{N}$ system quantum numbers. The corresponding pole is the first singularity to be found in t and u, respectively, when one moves away from the physical region for NN scattering $s \geq 4m^2$, $t \leq 0$, $u \leq 0$. The next singularity to be found, according to unitarity in this channel, is a cut corresponding to the two π-meson intermediate states. There is, in fact, a cut in t and in u along the real t and u axis. They extend from $t = 4\mu^2$ to $+\infty$ and from $u = 4\mu^2$ to $+\infty$. Other cuts start from $t = 9\mu^2$ and $u = 9\mu^2$ (3π-meson intermediate states), ...

For fixed s, t and u are easily expressed in terms of the cosine of the scattering angle in the NN center-of-mass system (1-20a, b).

$$t = -\frac{s - 4m^2}{2}(1 - \cos\theta)$$

$$u = -\frac{s - 4m^2}{2}(1 + \cos\theta)$$

As a function of the complex variable $\cos\theta$, the fixed s scattering amplitude has then two poles at

$$\cos\theta = \pm\left(1 + \frac{2\mu^2}{s - 4m^2}\right)$$

and two cuts along the real axis from $-\infty$ to $-1 - [8\mu^2/(s - 4m^2)]$ and from $1 + [8\mu^2/(s - 4m^2)]$ to $+\infty$. The physical values of the scattering amplitude correspond to the segment $-1 + 1$. It is obvious from Fig. 7-2 that, if forward or backward NN scattering is considered, the one-pion pole is much closer to the physical value considered than the two-pion cut. One may even expect that the one-pion exchange is a very important process in NN scattering as compared to many-pion exchange, the behavior of the physical amplitude being dominated by the nearest singularity. This would justify to

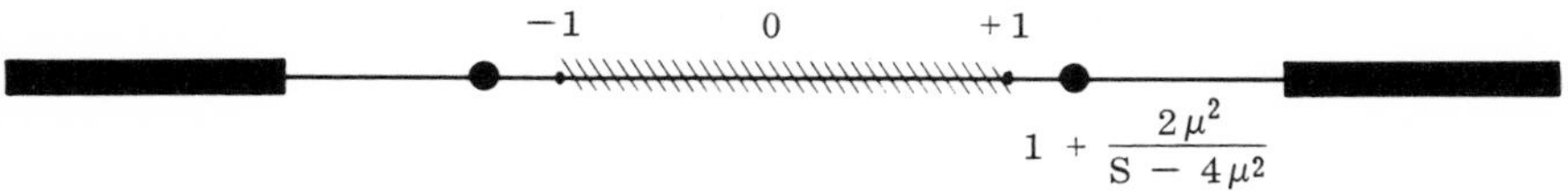

Figure 7-2

Cos θ plane. The hatched segment corresponds to the physical region.

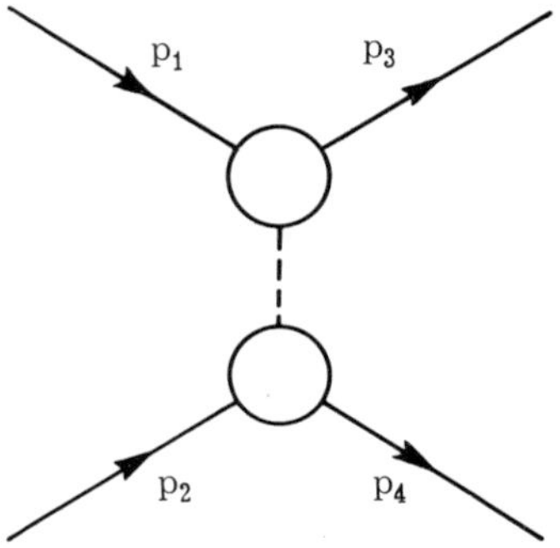

Figure 7-3

some extent lowest-order perturbation theory as applied to a particular case: forward scattering.

When s increases, the poles move closer to the physical region. This would enforce the validity of the approximation.

This is a pleasant prospect, since the one-pion exchange contribution to the scattering amplitude is the only one that can be obtained in a straightforward way in terms of the π-nucleon renormalized coupling constant (Fig. 7-3).

When one includes spin, the picture does not look so good though, since the cross section obtained from one-pion exchange alone is proportional to $t^2/(t - \mu)^2$ as it simply follows from the exchange of a pseudoscalar particle. It has a double zero at $\cos\theta = 1$. Therefore we cannot expect the one-pion exchange contribution to be dominant at any scattering angle.

7—2 CHEW-LOW EXTRAPOLATION SCHEME

For NN scattering the consideration of one-pion exchange only is not reliable. Nevertheless, the scattering amplitude has only the pole singularity in the t variable, up to $t = 4\mu^2$. Hence the scattering cross section times $(t - \mu^2)^2$ is free from singularities up to $t = 4\mu^2$, and a low-order polynomial should be reliable to approximate it in the physical region, and up to $t = \mu^2$. From extrapolation of measurements made for physical values of t, one then obtains the residue at the pole. The contribution of other terms in the extrapolated quantity obviously vanishes at $t = \mu^2$. The residue is equal to the product of the $N\pi \to N$ amplitudes which appear at each vertex, with all particles on their mass shell. The extrapolation procedure thus provides a further experimental determination of the π-nucleon coupling constant.[54]

This is quite similar to the procedure described to obtain the π-nucleon coupling constant from extrapolation of scattering data at fixed momentum transfer. Another technique has also been used to take advantage of the existence of this pole. It is the following.

We mentioned that the one-pion exchange could not be considered as a dominant process. Nevertheless the one-pion exchange contribution is the only well-known term in the scattering amplitude and, when expanded in partial wave, it obviously contributes to all ℓ values. Considering the scattering amplitude as the one-pion exchange contribution (Fig. 7-3) plus a sum of partial-wave contributions, one may then obtain a better fit to the scattering data. The one-pion exchange almost exhausts the higher waves (long-range interaction). More complicated and shorter-range processes are then expressed in terms of a small number of partial-wave amplitudes from which the contribution of the one-pion exchange term already considered is subtracted. This procedure has been applied successfully to the analysis of the 310-MeV data[55] and has lead to the elimination of spurious sets of phase shifts previously obtained when no proper attention was paid to the pole term.

If we now consider any reaction amplitude, we are lead to the following conjecture: Consider a process with n external lines. If it is possible to split the n particle that enter the reaction into a group of ingoing ones and a group of outgoing ones, having both the same quantum numbers as a particle of mass M, then the reaction amplitude, considered as an analytic function of the squared mass of either group of particles, has a pole at the value M^2. An ingoing particle can be considered as well as an outgoing antiparticle. Furthermore, the residue at the pole is given by the product of the two S-matrix elements connecting each group to the intermediate particle.

In order to illustrate this point, let us consider one-pion production in π-nucleon collisions (the $\pi + N \rightarrow 2\pi + N$ reaction). In such a production process, there are five independent scalar variables instead of two in elastic scattering. The $N\overline{N}$ and three-pion systems both have the same quantum numbers as one single pion and there is a pole in the momentum transfer variable at $t = \mu^2$. The one-pion exchange graph is shown in Fig. 5-3. The residue at the pole is the product of the π-nucleon coupling constant (lower vertex) by the $\pi\pi$ scattering amplitude since all particles are on their mass shells, $t = \mu^2$ (upper vertex). The next singularity in t, which is met as one moves away from the physical region (Fig. 7-4), is a cut related to three-pion intermediate states. One can then hope to obtain the $\pi\pi$ cross section from an extrapolation to $t = \mu^2$ of the measured cross section.

The contribution to the $\pi^- p \rightarrow \pi^- \pi^0 p$ cross section, say, of the one-pion exchange term alone is easily obtained

$$F = 2img\bar{u}(p')\gamma_5 u(p) \frac{1}{t - \mu^2} A(\omega, \cos\theta) \tag{7-3}$$

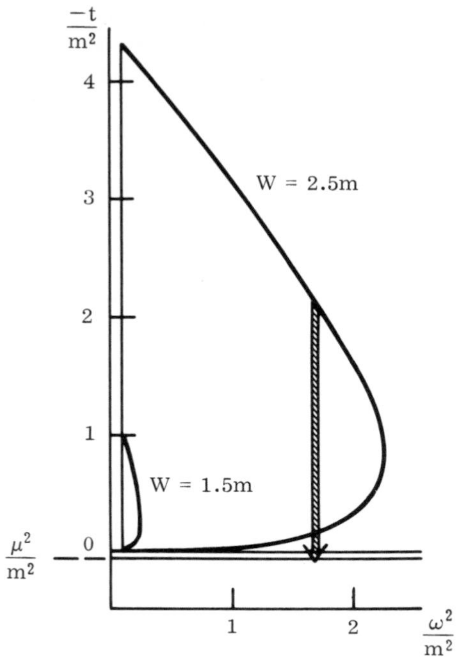

Figure 7-4

p (and p′) are the initial (and final) momentum of the proton. ω and θ the center-of-mass energy and scattering angle of the two π-mesons. $A(\omega, \cos\theta)$ is the $\pi\pi$ scattering amplitude. In fact, this is correct only at $t = \mu^2$ and we need otherwise an analytic continuation in t of the $\pi\pi$ amplitude. Nevertheless, since we are interested in an extrapolation to the pole, we simply write A in the expression for F. Similarly we simply take the π-nucleon coupling constant at the lower vertex. We have selected a particular charge state in order to avoid considering several charge amplitudes. We still have two spin amplitudes but we assume that the initial proton is not polarized, and that the polarization in the final state is not observed. The cross section corresponding to (7-3) is then given by

$$\frac{g^2}{4(2\pi)^5 qm} \int \delta(p + q - p' - q_1' - q_2') \frac{t}{(t - \mu^2)^2} |A|^2 \times \frac{d^3\mathbf{p}'\, d^3\mathbf{q}_1'\, d^3\mathbf{q}_2'}{8E'\omega_1'\omega_2'}$$

$q\omega_0$, $q_1'\,\omega_1'$, $q_2'\,\omega_2'$ are the momenta and energies of the initial and final

π-mesons; m, and E′, the initial, and final, nucleon energies. All variables are considered in the laboratory system. The integral is obviously Lorentz invariant. We write it as

$$\int \delta(P + q - p' - q_1' - q_2')\,\Theta(p_0')\ \delta(p'^2 + m^2)\,\Theta(q_{10}')\ \delta(q_1'^2 + \mu^2)$$

$$\times\ \Theta(q_{20}')\ \delta(q_2'^2 + \mu^2)\,\frac{t}{(t - \mu^2)^2}\,|A|^2\ d^4p'\ d^4q_1'\ d^4q_2'$$

Let us now consider a reference frame where $p + q - p'$ is along the time axis. This is obviously the two final mesons center-of-mass frame. We have

$$\int \Theta(p_0')\ \delta(p'^2 + m^2)\,\Theta(q_{10}')\ \delta(q_1'^2 + \mu^2)\ \delta(\omega^2 - 2\omega\omega_1')$$

$$\times\ \frac{t}{(t - \mu^2)^2}\ |A|^2\ d^4p'\ d\mathbf{q}_1'\ d\omega_1'$$

The integrals on $d^3\mathbf{q}_1'$ and $d\omega_1'$ are now easily performed using the last two δ-functions. The integral over the π direction gives the $\pi\pi$ scattering cross section

$$\sigma_{\pi\pi}(\omega) = \int d\Omega\,\left|\frac{A}{8\pi\omega}\right|^2$$

One gets

$$\sigma = \frac{g^2}{4\pi}\,\frac{1}{2\pi q m}\int \omega\sigma_{\pi\pi}(\omega)\sqrt{\frac{\omega^2}{4} - \mu^2}\ \frac{t}{(t - \mu^2)^2}$$

$$\times\ p'\ dE'\ d\cos\theta_{p'}$$

where $\theta_{p'}$ is the nucleon recoil angle.

With the laboratory system expressions $t = 2m(m - E')$ and $\omega^2 = (\omega_0 + m)^2 + m^2 + 2p'q\cos\theta_{p'} - 2E' \times (\omega_0 + m)$, one switches to the more convenient t and ω^2 variables and obtains

$$\frac{\partial^2\sigma}{\partial t\,\partial\omega^2} = \frac{1}{2\pi q^2}\,\frac{g^2}{4\pi}\,\frac{t}{4m^2}\,\omega\sqrt{\frac{\omega^2}{4} - \mu^2}\ \frac{\sigma_{\pi\pi}(\omega)}{(t - \mu^2)^2} \qquad (7\text{-}4)$$

As emphasized earlier, this is however true only at $t = \mu^2$ (all 4π-mesons on their mass shell). The actual differential cross section has besides (7-4) a term with a single pole at $t = \mu^2$ and a term regular at $t = \mu^2$. They do not contribute, however, to $(t - \mu^2)^2 \times (\partial^2\sigma/\partial t\ \partial\omega^2)$ extrapolated at $t = \mu^2$. Therefore we obtain an exact relation:

$$\sigma_{\pi\pi}(\omega) = \lim_{t \to \mu^2} \left\{ \frac{2\pi q^2 (t - \mu^2)^2}{(g^2/4\pi)(t/4m^2)\omega\sqrt{(\omega^2/4) - \mu^2}} \frac{\partial^2 \sigma}{\partial t\, \partial \omega^2} \right\} \qquad (7\text{-}5)$$

This extrapolation procedure provides a determination of quantities otherwise not accessible at present. Figure 7-4 shows the physical region and the extrapolation distances for two energies. We no longer have a simple straight line fit. What is actually done is to try a polynomial expansion in t, with the hope that the function is sufficiently well behaved.

7–3 PERIPHERAL MODEL

Although π-nucleon inelastic collisions have been extensively studied, data are not yet accurate enough to allow a reliable extrapolation. Though the pole is very close to the limit of the physical region its contribution to $(t - \mu^2)^2(\partial^2\sigma/\partial t\,\partial\omega^2)$ goes through zero at $t = 0$. The extrapolated value, therefore, strongly depends upon the fit selected for the physical values of the differential cross sections. What has been done so far is to analyze the data for physical values of t with the pole at $t = \mu^2$ assumed to be the dominant feature. One goes beyond polology and makes a dynamical hypothesis.

If one selects only the events for which $|t|$ is small ($-t \leq 8\mu^2$, say, for 1.6 BeV/c incident pion), one can hope that the one-pion exchange process is an important production mechanism and, when $\sigma_{\pi\pi}$ is large, the most important one. Data are then analyzed in terms of relation (7-4) and an approximate value of $\sigma_{\pi\pi}$ is thus obtained. Since the $\pi\pi$ interaction actually shows two resonances, the ρ and the f^0, this simple approach actually works and led to the discovery of these two new mesons as discussed in Chapter 5. If only low momentum transfer events are kept, one verifies that the cross section obtained this way is rather like what one would expect for a p-wave resonance. This is illustrated by Fig. 7-5. Such an approximation is referred to as a peripheral model calculation.

Figure 7-5 gives $\pi\pi$ mass spectra obtained for $1.5 < -t/\mu^2 < 8$ (solid line) and for $8 < -t/\mu^2 < 25.5$ (dashed line). The ρ is clearly seen only in the low momentum transfer data.

Lacking data accurate enough for an extrapolation procedure to be reliable one can look for processes for which the pole contribution should be, by all odds, the dominant one. In other words one can try to select events for which a Born approximation calculation could be, on kinematical grounds, a good enough approximation.

Let us consider as an example the process shown on Fig. 7-6. It corresponds to the reaction $\gamma + p \to \pi^+ + (n)$, where (n) denotes an arbitrary final state with two or more particles. This was first proposed by Drell.[56] At the lower vertex we have the π-nucleon

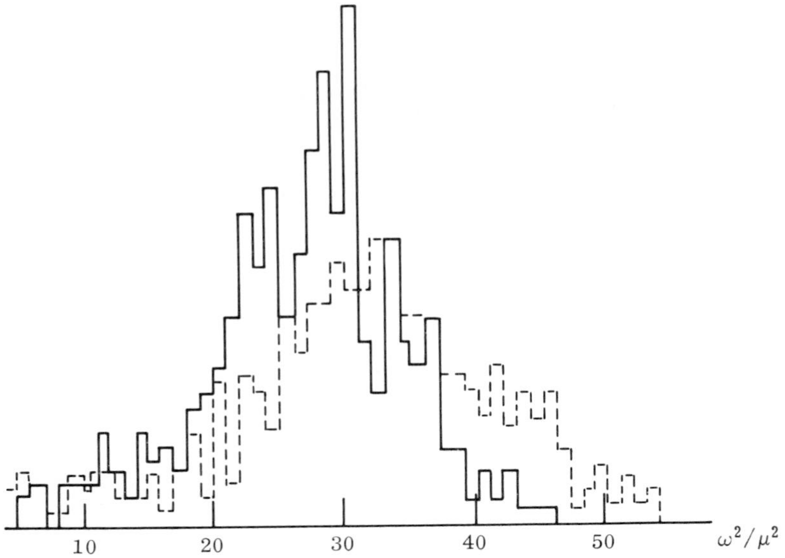

Figure 7-5

reaction amplitude that gives a large contribution for physical values of t instead of the π-nucleon vertex that gives a contribution proportional to t in the cross section which we had previously considered in the $\pi + N \to 2\pi + N$ reaction. The cross section obtained from this graph alone reads

$$\frac{\partial^2 \sigma}{\partial t \ \partial \omega^2} = \frac{\alpha}{2\pi} \frac{\sin^2 \theta}{(1 - (q/\omega)\cos\theta)^2} \frac{\omega(k - \omega)}{4\pi k^3} \times \sigma_{tot}(k - \omega) \tag{7-6}$$

where θ is the π^+ production angle, q and ω its momentum and energy (ω is assumed to be large as compared to μ). k is the momentum of the incident photon. All quantities are defined in the laboratory system. $\sigma_{tot}(k - \omega)$ is the total πN cross section at the π^- laboratory energy $k - \omega$. The (n) final state is supposed not to be observed, and a summation over all possible states is performed. The actual π-nucleon cross section enters only when all particles are on their mass shells (after extrapolation to the pole). One can consider (7-6) as a reliable expression for forward angles and high-energy ($\omega \gg \mu$) events, so that the denominator in (7-6) is very small.

This peripheral approximation has been checked experimentally.[56] The resonance behavior of the π-nucleon cross section does show up

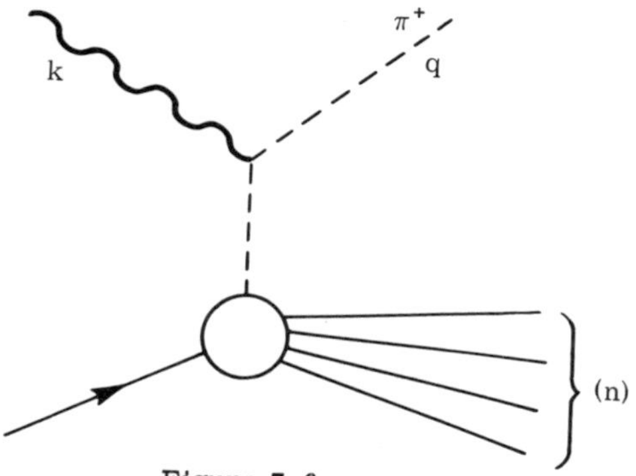

Figure 7-6

in the data as expected from (7-6). The $p + p \rightarrow p + n + \pi^+$ reaction at 1-2 BeV is another example where the peripheral model (one-pion exchange graph) gives good results.[57] This process seems, however, to become negligible as compared to diffraction dissociation at higher energy. In the Regge formalism, the one-pion exchange should, in fact, not be important at high energies since the π-trajectory in the physical region for scattering is below the $\alpha = 0$ axis.[40]

7—4 THE YANG-TREIMAN TEST

The examples just considered show that in the 1-3 BeV region events can be selected in such a way that the one-pion exchange contribution may be dominant. Since the one-pion exchange mechanism is liable to provide measurements of otherwise unattainable quantities, it is of great interest to check, as thoroughly as possible, whether it is actually predominant. A necessary condition to be fulfilled, for a one-pion exchange process, is the following.[58] Consider the cross section corresponding to the graph of Fig. 7-7 alone. It reads

$$J\sigma = \Pi_i \Pi_j \int |G(p,p_i')|^2 \; |H(k,k_j')|^2 \frac{1}{(t-\mu^2)^2} \; d^4p_i' \; d^4k_j'$$
$$\times \; \delta\left(p + k - \sum_i p_i' - \sum_j k_j'\right) \Theta(p_{io}') \; \delta(p_i'^2 + m^2)$$
$$\times \; \Theta\left(k_{jo}'\right) \delta\left(k_j'^2 + m^2 j\right) \qquad (7\text{-}7)$$

where J is the incident flux. The symbol Π_i stands for a product at all terms labeled by "i." The very important fact that the amplitude

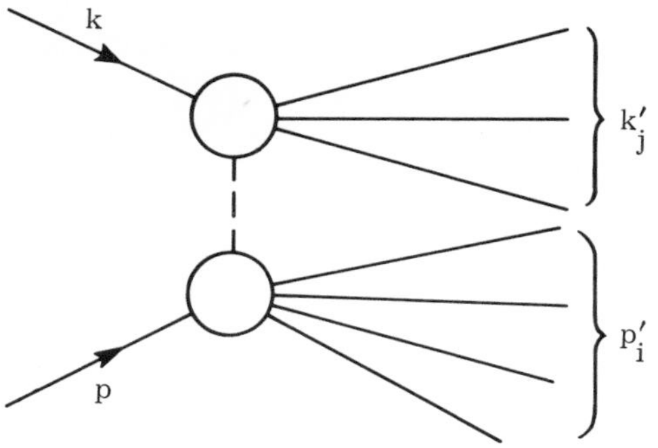

Figure 7-7

factors out into two terms, which refer, respectively, to the upper and lower vertices, is a consequence of the exchange of one single, spin-zero particle.

Now consider the frame of reference in which $\mathbf{p}$ (or $\mathbf{k}$) is equal to zero. $G(p,p'_i)$ [or $H(k,k'_j)$] will then be invariant by rotation of all the $\mathbf{p}'_i$ (or $\mathbf{k}'_j$) vectors, and σ will be invariant under this rotation if nothing changes in (7-7). Hence, if the rotation is performed around the momentum transfer direction, $\mathbf{q} = \Sigma_i \mathbf{p}_i$ $(= -\Sigma_j \mathbf{k}'_j)$ will not change.

If we consider the $\pi + N \to 2\pi + N$ reaction the distribution of the final π-mesons in the initial π-meson rest frame must be invariant under rotation around $(\mathbf{p}' - \mathbf{p})$.

The property is also true if we rotate all $\mathbf{p}'_i$ (or $\mathbf{k}'_j$) around $\mathbf{q}$ in the frame of reference where $\Sigma_i \mathbf{p}'_i$ (or $\Sigma_j \mathbf{k}'_j$) is zero.

Such tests can be extended to the exchange of a particle arbitrary spin. The experimental checks are, of course, more involved.[59]

7–5 NEW MESONS POLOLOGY

We have seen that, in some particular cases, the pole term alone gives a good approximation to the physical reaction amplitude. We are then going into the dynamics of the process, whereas the extrapolation procedure involved almost nothing about the actual dynamics. Furthermore the dynamics is very simple in these particular cases, since a single graph gives a fairly good answer.

We have considered so far only one-pion exchange. In many processes though, such as π-nucleon scattering, the lowest mass state that can be exchanged (it corresponds to the nearest singularity in the $N\bar{N}$ annihilation channel) is a two-pion state. This follows from Lorentz invariance. (The next one is a four-pion state as follows from charge independence.)

Nevertheless there is a $\pi\pi$ resonance in the isotopic spin-1 state and one may hope that the $T = 1$ two-pion exchange processes could be "summarized" in considering only the exchange of the resonance. The resonance, or the meson, is then treated as a stable particle. As a matter of fact good results are obtained.[60]

An important topic that illustrates very well this new technique is the analysis of the nucleon form factors. They define the virtual photon nucleon vertex; the nucleon current is written as[61]

$$j_\mu = \bar{u}(P_f)\left\{\gamma_\mu F_1(t) + \sigma_{\mu\nu} q^\nu \frac{1}{2m} F_2(t)\right\} u(P_i) \qquad (7\text{-}8)$$

where $-t = q^2$ is the nucleon momentum transfer. F_1 and F_2 are the usual Dirac and Fermi nucleon form factors. They are usually combined into an isotopic-scalar and an isotopic-vector form factor, $F_i^S = F_i^p + F_i^n$ and $F_i^V = F_i^p - F_i^n$.

They are supposed to satisfy dispersion relations in t which are written as

$$F_1^{V,S} = \frac{e}{2} - \frac{t}{\pi}\int_{t_0}^{\infty} \frac{\text{Im } F_1^{V,S}(t')\, dt'}{t'(t' - t)}$$

$$F_2^{V,S} = e\,\frac{\mu_p \mp \mu_n}{2} - \frac{t}{\pi}\int_{t_0}^{\infty} \frac{\text{Im } F_2^{V,S}(t')\, dt'}{t'(t' - t)} \qquad (7\text{-}9)$$

μ_p (and μ_n) is the proton (and neutron) gyromagnetic ratio. In effect, a subtraction does not seem to be required for the Fermi form factor.

As shown in Chapter 3, the lowest mass state to be found is a two-pion (and three-pion) state for the isotopic vector (and isotopic scalar) form factors. Therefore, the imaginary part is zero up to $t = 4\mu^2$ for F^V and up to $t = 9\mu^2$ for F^S.

We first consider the isotopic vector form factors. Since the physical values of the form factors for electron-nucleon scattering refer to $t \leq 0$, the 2π intermediate state is expected to give the main contribution to the dispersion integrals. For $4\mu^2 \leq t < 16\mu^2$ only two mesons intermediate have to be considered in the unitarity relation (1-24) extended down to these values of t. One gets

$$\text{Im } F_i^V = \frac{e}{2}\left(\frac{t}{4} - \mu^2\right)\sqrt{1 - \frac{4\mu^2}{t}}\; F_\pi^* \Gamma_i$$

since the exchanged photon implies that the intermediate state has angular momentum 1.

F_π is the $\gamma \to 2\pi$ amplitude, i.e., the π-meson form factor. Γ_1 is the $\pi\pi \to N\overline{N}$ amplitude. It has to be defined by analytic continuation from $t \geq 4m^2$ down to $t \geq 4\mu^2$.

Dispersion relations in t are written for F_π and Γ_i and the only intermediate state retained in the unitarity relations is consistently the two-pion state. In both cases the $\pi\pi$ scattering amplitude now enters in the $T = 1$, $j = 1$ state.

The whole procedure has been developed by Frazer and Fulco.[43] They worked backward from the isovector form factors to $\pi\pi$ scattering and were led to assume a $\pi\pi$ resonance, the later-discovered ρ-meson.

With this result in hand, however, one can obtain a fairly good fit to the experimental data with much less labor. If the resonance is narrow F_π and Γ_i have a sharp maximum at the resonance energy (the ρ-meson mass). The important contribution to the dispersion integrals comes from values of t' close to m_ρ^2. Let us even write the imaginary part of the form factor as a δ-function at $t = m_\rho^2$. We obtain

$$F_1^V(t) \simeq \frac{e}{2}\left(1 + \frac{at}{t - m_\rho^2}\right) \tag{7-10}$$

with a similar relation for F_2. At present such simple relations are not in disagreement with the data.[62]

In other words, what we have actually done with such approximations, is to assume that the virtual photon is coupled to the nucleon through a ρ-meson. This is a new kind of perturbation calculation in which resonances would enter as particles. The isotopic vector form factor is then written in the following way:

$$F_i^V(t) = \frac{g^i_{N\overline{N}\rho}\, g_{\gamma\rho}}{t - m_\rho^2} + C$$

The first term is the contribution of the "ρ exchange" graph. $g^i_{N\overline{N}\rho}$ (and $g_{\gamma\rho}$) are the ρ-nucleon (and photon-ρ) coupling constants (Fig. 7-8). C stands for the contribution of all the other terms. It is assumed to depend very weakly on t. This is identical to (7-10).

Such drastic approximations may be reliable because one calculates the form factors for $t \leq 0$ only. Nevertheless $m_\rho^2 = 29\mu^2$ is not very small after all, and contribution from 4π- and 6π-meson intermediate states may not be negligible. They cannot be incorporated in the unitarity relation with present calculation techniques.

Similar problems are met with the 3π-meson intermediate state which is the first to be found in the isotopic scalar case. Nevertheless, similar approximations may be of some help. Since there is a

3π resonance with isotopic spin 0 and angular momentum 1 (the ω-meson) we may try a simple γ-nucleon coupling through an ω. Namely,

$$F_1^S \simeq \frac{e}{2}\left(1 + \frac{Gt}{t - m_\omega^2}\right)$$

with, maybe, also a contribution from the φ_0.

With almost the same masses, for the ρ and ω this may help us to understand the absence of charge distribution of the neutron[61] $(F_1^n = F_1^S - F_1^V)$.

With the numerous resonances found so far, the importance of such simple processes may lead to a new kind of perturbation theory. Nevertheless, with large coupling constant, one must be very careful not to violate unitarity. This is quickly done when one considers single graphs.

To conclude let us note that, even with plain polology, some troubles are found. Consider, for instance, the graph of Fig. 7-9: scattering of two equal-mass spinless particles, with exchange of a meson of spin j, and mass M. The scattering amplitude has a pole at $t = M^2$ and its residue is $C\ P_j(\cos\theta_t)$ where C is a constant and θ_t the scattering angle in the crossed reaction. As follows from (1-20)

$$\cos\theta_t = 1 + \frac{2s}{t - 4m^2}$$

Therefore we write the scattering amplitude as

$$A(s,t,u) = C\,\frac{P_j\left[1 + (2s/(t - 4m^2))\right]}{t - M^2} + A'(s,t,u)$$

where A′ is regular at $t = M^2$.

The first term behaves asymptotically in s as s^j. This alone would correspond to a cross section proportional to $s^{2(j-1)}$. This is

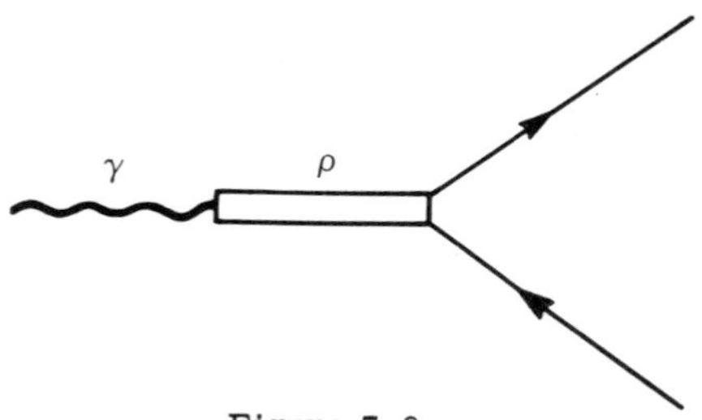

Figure 7-8

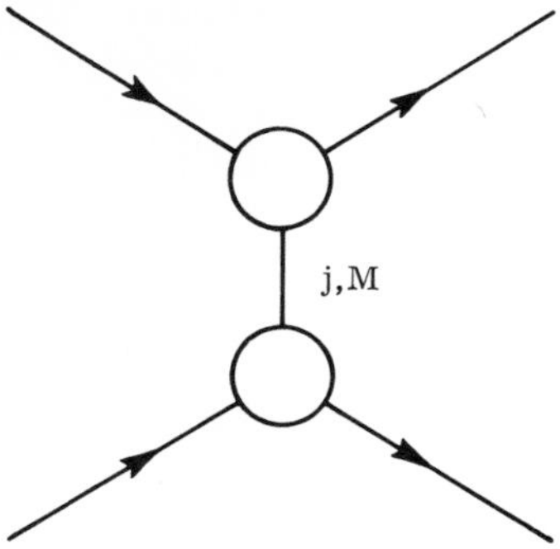

Figure 7-9

a paradoxical situation since, on the one hand, there exist high spin particles and, on the other hand, cross sections seem to tend toward constant values at infinity. This is one of the motivations for the introduction of Regge poles in strong-interaction physics.

REFERENCES

REFERENCES

1. M. L. Goldberger in "Les Houches Lecture Notes, 1960," Hermann, Paris; R. Omnès, ibid.
2. J. D. Jackson, in "Dispersion Relations," G. R. Screaton (ed.), Interscience, New York, 1961.
3. G. F. Chew, M. L. Goldberger, F. E. Low, and Y. Nambu, *Phys. Rev.*, **106**, 1377 (1957).
4. S. Mandelstam, *Phys. Rev.*, **112**, 1344 (1958); **115**, 1741 (1959).
5. M. Jacob and G. C. Wick, *Ann. Phys. (N.Y.)*, **7**, 404 (1959).
6. E. Wigner, "Group Theory and Its Application to the Quantum Mechanics of Atomic Spectra," Academic Press, New York, 1959.
7. We use the notation of M. E. Rose, "Elementary Theory of Angular Momentum," Wiley, New York, 1957.
8. S. Schweber, "An Introduction to Relativistic Quantum Field Theory," Row, Peterson, Evanston, Illinois, 1961, pp. 212 and 237.
9. L. Michel, *Nuovo Cimento*, **10**, 319 (1953); T. D. Lee and C. N. Yang, *Nuovo Cimento*, **3**, 749 (1956).
10. We do not discuss the low-energy phase shifts. See J. Orear, "CERN Symposium, 1958," p. 43; J. Hamilton and W. S. Woolcock, *Phys. Rev.*, **118**, 291 (1960).
11. G. C. Wick, *Rev. Mod. Phys.*, **27**, 339 (1955); G. F. Chew, in "Encyclopedia of Physics," S. Flügge (ed.), vol. 43, Springer, Berlin (to be published).
12. P. Falk-Vairant and G. Valladas, *Rev. Mod. Phys.*, **33**, 362 (1961); B. J. Mayer, *Rev. Mod. Phys.*, **33**, 367 (1961); and for higher energy data, A. N. Diddens et al., *Phys. Rev. Letters*, **10**, 262 (1963).
13. R. Omnès and G. Valladas, "Proceedings of the Aix en Provence Conference on Elementary Particles, 1961," p. 467.
14. G. Höhler et al., "Proceedings of the Aix en Provence

Conference on Elementary Particles, 1961," p. 485.
15. R. L. Walker, "Proceedings of the 1960 Conference on High Energy Physics," p. 17; R. Peierls, *Phys. Rev.*, **118**, 325 (1960).
16. B. T. Feld and W. Layson, "Proceedings of the Geneva Conference on High Energy Physics, 1962," p. 147.
17. W. Frazer and J. Ball, *Phys. Rev. Letters*, **7**, 204 (1961); L. F. Cook and B. W. Lee, *Phys. Rev.*, **127**, 297 (1962). See also S. Mandelstam, J. Paton, R. Peierls, and A. Sarker, *Ann. Phys. (N.Y.)*, **18**, 198 (1962), for a still different interpretation.
18. M. Froissart, *Nuovo Cimento*, **22**, 191 (1961).
19. J. F. Detoeuf et al., "Proceedings of the Geneva Conference on High Energy Physics, 1962," p. 7.
20. K. M. Watson, *Phys. Rev.*, **88**, 1163 (1952).
21. S. Lindenbaum and R. Steinheimer, *Phys. Rev.*, **109**, 1723 (1958).
22. J. Meyer et al. "Proceedings of the Aix en Provence Conference on Elementary Particles, 1961," p. 27.
23. L. S. Rodberg, *Phys. Rev.*, **106**, 1090 (1957).
24. H. J. Schnytzer, Thesis, Rochester University, 1960.
25. B. Gregory, "Proceedings of the Geneva Conference on High Energy Physics, 1962," p. 779; G. Snow, ibid., p. 795.
26. M. Gell-Mann, California Institute of Technology, *Rept. CTSL-20*, 1961.
27. A. H. Rosenfeld and S. L. Glashow, *Phys. Rev. Letters*, **10**, 192 (1963); G. Puppi, "Proceedings of the Geneva Conference on High Energy Physics, 1962," p. 712.
28. B. Maglic et al., *Phys. Rev. Letters*, **7**, 178 (1962).
29. A. Pevsner et al., *Phys. Rev. Letters*, **7**, 421 (1962).
30. A. Erwin et al., *Phys. Rev. Letters*, **6**, 628 (1961).
31. W. Selove et al., *Phys. Rev. Letters*, **9**, 272 (1962); J. J. Veillet et al., *Phys. Rev. Letters*, **10**, 29 (1963).
32. P. L. Connoly et al., *Phys. Rev. Letters*, **10**, 371 (1963); P. Schlein et al., *Phys. Rev. Letters*, **10**, 368 (1963).
33. M. Alston et al., *Phys. Rev. Letters*, **6**, 300 (1961).
34. M. Gell-Mann, D. Sharp, and W. Wagner, *Phys. Rev. Letters*, **8**, 71 (1962); I. Yu. Kolzarev and L. B. Okun, "Proceedings of the Geneva Conference on High Energy Physics, 1962," p. 173.
35. R. Armenteros et al., "Proceedings of the Geneva Conference on High Energy Physics, 1962," p. 90.
36. C. Alff et al., *Phys. Rev. Letters*, **9**, 325 (1962).
37. M. Chretien et al., *Phys. Rev. Letters*, **9**, 127 (1962).
38. C. Fowler et al., *Phys. Rev. Letters*, **10**, 110 (1963).
39. Orsay, Saclay, Bari, Bologna, *Nuovo Cimento*, **25**, 365 (1962).
40. G. F. Chew and S. Frautschi, *Phys. Rev. Letters*, **7**, 394 (1961); Lovelace, "Proceedings of the Geneva Conference on High Energy Physics, 1962," p. 510.
41. K. J. Foley et al., *Phys. Rev. Letters*, **10**, 376 (1963).

42. R. Armenteros et al., "Proceedings of the Geneva Conference on High Energy Physics, 1962," p. 295; M. Schwartz, *Phys. Rev. Letters*, **6**, 656 (1961).
43. W. Frazer and J. Fulco, *Phys. Rev.* **117**, 1609 (1960).
44. J. J. Sakurai, Preprint, University of Chicago.
45. A. Abashian, N. Booth, and K. Crowe, *Phys. Rev. Letters*, **5**, 258 (1960).
46. H. Lehmann, *Nuovo Cimento*, **10**, 579 (1958).
47. A review of most recent works including the effect of $\pi\pi$ interaction would have been outside the scope of these notes. We refer the reader to J. Hamilton and W. S. Woolcock, Determination of pion-nucleon parameters and phase shifts from dispersion relations, *Rev. Mod. Phys.*, **35**, 737 (1963). See also Hamilton et al., "Proceedings of the Geneva Conference on High Energy Physics, 1962," p. 159.
48. J. V. Lepore and K. M. Watson, *Phys. Rev.*, **76**, 1157 (1949).
49. U. Haber-Schaim, *Phys. Rev.*, **104**, 1193 (1956).
50. H. D. Noyes and D. N. Edwards, *Phys. Rev.*, **118**, 1409 (1960).
51. I. Ia. Pomeranchuk, *JETP*, **34**, 499 (1958).
52. G. F. Chew, M. L. Goldberger, F. E. Low, and Y. Nambu, *Phys. Rev.*, **106**, 1345 (1957).
53. W. Davidon and M. L. Goldberger, *Phys. Rev.*, **104**, 1119 (1956).
54. G. F. Chew and F. E. Low, *Phys. Rev.*, **113**, 1640 (1959).
55. M. Moravcsik, in "Dispersion Relations," G. R. Screaton (ed.), Interscience, New York, 1961.
56. S. D. Drell, *Rev. Mod. Phys.*, **33**, 458 (1961). We do not discuss more complicated processes than the one-particle exchange, see Amati, Fubini, Stanghelini, and Tonin, *Nuovo Cimento*, **22**, 569 (1961).
57. F. Selleri, *Phys. Rev. Letters*, **6**, 64 (1961).
58. C. N. Yang and S. Treiman, *Phys. Rev. Letters*, **8**, 140 (1962).
59. M. Gourdin and A. Martin, CERN 3568/Th. 261; D. Bessis et al., *Nuovo Cimento*, **27**, 376 (1963).
60. J. Bowcok, N. Cottingham, and D. Lurie, *Phys. Rev. Letters*, **5**, 386 (1960).
61. See, for instance, S. Drell and F. Zachariasen, "Electromagnetic Structure of the Nucleons," Oxford, New York, 1959.
62. G. R. Bishop, "Proceedings of the Geneva Conference on High Energy Physics, 1962," p. 753; S. Fubini, ibid., p. 765.
63. V. E. Barnes et al., *Phys. Rev. Letters*, **12**, 204 (1964).
64. N. Gelfand et al., *Phys. Rev. Letters*, **11**, 436 (1963).

NUCLEAR DEMOCRACY
AND BOOTSTRAP DYNAMICS

PREFACE

Three years ago in my preface to an earlier contribution in this same series *(The S-matrix Theory of Strong Interactions)* the hope was expressed that an axiomatic basis for S-matrix theory would soon develop. Since that time, there has been progress in the direction of axioms but a solid foundation is still lacking. Strong interaction physics nevertheless has continued to evolve, even without axioms, and my contribution to this book may be regarded as a sequel to the previous lectures written in the same spirit. Students seeking a well-defined theory will not find it here; they will find a certain point of view.

The distinguishing characteristic of these new lectures, which were given first at the University of Cambridge and then revised for presentation at the Middle East Technical University in Ankara, is the unequivocal adoption of nuclear democracy as a guiding principle. The previous lectures discussed the conjecture that all strongly interacting particles, from the least massive up to excited states of transuranic nuclei, may stand on a dynamically equivalent basis; but the conservative influence of Lagrangian field theory may be seen in those lectures in the handling of subtraction terms and arbitrary parameters in general. The point of view here is that subtractions can always be avoided and that no arbitrary parameters should appear in the strong interaction S-matrix.

It is too soon to say with absolute certainty that there are no aristocrats among nuclear particles; theorists continue to investigate, for example, the possibility that certain spin-one mesons may play a distinguished role analogous to that of the photon, with arbitrary mass and coupling constant. My standpoint here, however, is that every nuclear particle should receive equal treatment under the law.

I want to express my gratitude to Dr. J. R. Taylor and Dr. M. McMillan for the lecture notes which formed the basis for the present material. I am also grateful to Professor Feza Gürsey for encouragement to develop this material for publication.

Geoffrey Chew

Berkeley, California
April 1964

INTRODUCTION

SINCE the publication in 1961 of my volume of lectures on the S-matrix theory of strong interactions,[1] the concept of democracy among nuclear particles has received encouragement from both experimental and theoretical developments. The term "nuclear democracy," suggested by Gell-Mann, describes the conjecture that all strongly interacting particles are composite (bound) states, owing their existence entirely to forces of the general type originally proposed by Yukawa. This concept was introduced in the earlier lectures but an effort was made there to leave open the possibility that some strongly interacting particles might after all be more "fundamental" than others. A consequence of such a cautious approach was a lack of clarity, particularly as regards arbitrary parameters in the S matrix. My purpose in the present lectures is to review key aspects of the S-matrix theory of strong interactions that are directly affected by the conjecture of nuclear democracy. These aspects are dynamical rather than kinematical and will lead us quickly to a consideration of the "bootstrap" mechanism and Regge poles, which were only briefly mentioned in the earlier volume. Kinematical material covered in the previous lectures, or in the preceding article by Jacob, will not be repeated here, but a brief review of basic kinematics is given in Chapter 1. It will be assumed that the reader is familiar with the idea of analytic continuation in angular momentum, as covered, for example, in Ref. 17.

The revolutionary character of nuclear particle democracy is best appreciated by contrasting the aristocratic structure of atomic physics as governed by quantum electrodynamics. No attempt is made there to explain the existence and properties of the electron and the photon; one has always accepted their masses, spins, etc., together with the fine-structure constant, as given parameters. There exist composite atomic particles, such as positronium, whose properties *are* calculable from the forces holding them together, but so far one does not see a plausible basis, even in principle, for computing the properties of photon and electron as we compute those of positronium. In particular the zero photon mass and the small magnitude of the fine-structure constant appear unlikely to emerge purely from dynamics. Among strongly interacting particles, on the other hand, we have yet to see very small masses or other properties that cannot plausibly be attributed to a dynamical origin.

The bootstrap concept is tightly bound up with the notion of a democracy governed by dynamics. Each nuclear particle is conjectured to be a bound state of those S-matrix channels with which it communicates, arising from forces associated with the exchange of particles that communicate with "crossed" channels. (The principle of crossing is reviewed in Chapter 1.) Each of these latter particles in turn owes *its* existence to a set of forces to which the original particle makes a contribution. In other words, each particle helps to generate other particles which in turn generate it. In this circular and violently nonlinear situation we shall see that quite plausibly *no* free parameters appear, the only self-consistent set of strongly interacting particles being the one we find in nature.

If the system is in fact self-determining perhaps the special strong-interaction symmetries are not arbitrarily to be imposed. No convincing explanation has yet been given for the origin of isotopic spin, strangeness, or the newly discovered eightfold way, but many physicists believe that the secret will emerge from requirements of self-consistency in a democracy. Hopefully the origin of these symmetries will be understood at the same moment we understand the pattern of masses and spins for strongly interacting particles—both aspects of the system emerging from the dynamics of the bootstrap.

It must be stated at once that S-matrix theory is not yet sufficiently mature to allow a systematic assault on the bootstrap problem. The approach at present is to assume the existence of certain particles and symmetries and then to see what other particles and symmetries are thereby implied, as well as whether the original assumption is dynamically consistent with its consequences. In playing this game, approximations must be made, the basic assumption always being that singularities of the S-matrix sufficiently "distant" from the starting point may be neglected. (See Chap. 1 or Ref. 1.) The difficulty is that for most channels the singularity structure is so intricate that one is at present not quite sure what "distant" means. The meaning is fairly clear for a significant number of two-body channels, and it is here that we shall concentrate our attention, but the unraveling of the general topology of S-matrix singularities remains a key issue. This puzzle must be solved, at least in principle, if the dynamics is to have a solid foundation. The current rate of progress, as discussed in Chapter 1, allows one to hope that a solution will be forthcoming.

Even if one is optimistic about the development of a firm S-matrix framework for the nuclear bootstrap, one cannot help wondering why particle democracy should fail to encompass the photon and the leptons. My personal guess with respect to the photon is that this particle plays a unique and essential role in the connection between the concepts of energy-momentum and macroscopic space-time. S-matrix theory in the sense of these lectures never makes contact with the space-time concept; only the energy-momentum continuum is employed. But ultimately the definition (as well as the actual measurement) of momentum involves space and time in a macroscopic, coarse grained, sense. All experiments that actually measure momenta share two striking characteristics: (1) They cannot be described in a pure S-matrix framework, precisely because their description requires the space-time concept. (2) They always depend on electromagnetic interactions. A little thought suggests that it may be impossible, even in principle, to perform a momentum measurement without making use of the long-range forces characteristic of electromagnetism. Thus the zero photon mass, which makes this long range possible, perhaps is essential to the very definition of momentum, playing a role that cannot be filled by any of the strongly interacting particles. By the same token since electromagnetism permits the performance of experiments that have no S-matrix description, why should we expect the photon (i.e., electromagnetism) to emerge from a pure S-matrix framework?

An answer to such questions may only be possible when we have achieved a better grasp of precisely what is meant by a physical measurement of the position of a particle and the time at which the measurement is performed. The role of the observer here may be an essential one. To quote from a recent lecture of Wigner,[2] "There are many signs which portend that a more profound understanding of the phenomenon of observation and cognition, together with an appreciation of the limits of our ability to understand, is a not-too-distant future step. At any rate, it should be the next decisive breakthrough toward a more integrated understanding of the world..."

For the present we may console ourselves by recalling the historical circumstance that nature has so far revealed her secrets in a set of remarkably well-separated installments. Why, no one understands, but she has done so in the past and at present seems to be repeating the pattern by inviting us to understand strong interactions as a more or less isolated collection of phenomena. All the evidence suggests that nuclear particles owe their existence to the strong forces acting between them, with electromagnetism as well as weak interactions acting only as a small perturbation.

1

MAXIMAL ANALYTICITY OF THE FIRST DEGREE

A mathematically unambiguous set of S-matrix axioms has not yet been achieved, but the difficulties stem from singularities that are in any event still ignored in practical calculations. The rule appears to be that as soon as a particular singularity is recognized as having physical importance the mathematical nature of the singularity quickly becomes clarified. By now certain general statements about the S-matrix have become accepted as true in this spirit. That is, they have survived a number of different stages in the extension of our understanding of the physical content of singularities and seem a good bet to survive indefinitely. We shall now list ten statements of this kind, with the understanding that a logically ordered, mathematically precise, and nonredundant set of axioms is not the object. Our concern is only with what we hope to be the true state of affairs.

1. S-matrix elements depend upon incoming and outgoing particle momenta and spin orientations in a manner consistent with the requirements of special relativity. This condition, emphasized first by Heisenberg, has recently been formulated with generality and precision by Stapp[3]; it is usually referred to as "Lorentz invariance."

2. Every S-matrix element can be separated into products of "connected parts," each multiplied by the appropriate energy-momentum conservation δ-functions. Thus, for example, the element describing the reaction a + b + c → a + b + d contains the following three products:

(i) $\xrightarrow{a}\ \delta(p_a^i - p_a^f) \times$ 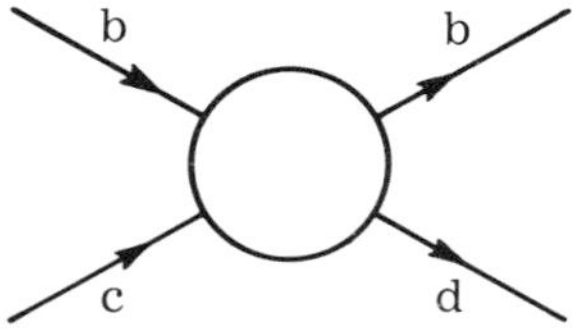

$\delta(p_b^i + p_c - p_b^f - p_d)$

(ii) $\overset{b}{\rightarrow}\ \delta(p_b^i - p_b^f) \times$ 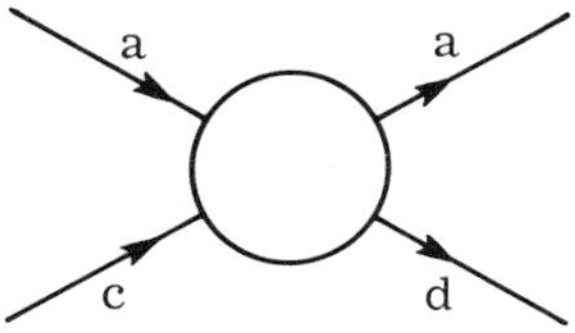

$\delta(p_a^i + p_c - p_a^f - p_d)$

(iii) 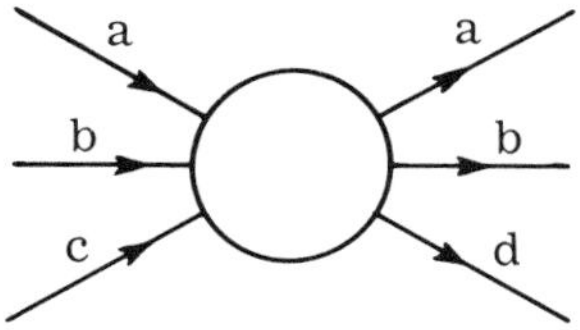

$\delta(p_a^i + p_b^i + p_c - p_a^f - p_b^f - p_d)$

where the symbols with arrows attached designate what are called "connected parts."‡ The physical significance of the first product in this example is that it is the amplitude of the probability for the reaction to occur with nothing happening to particle a but interaction between the others. In the second product nothing happens to b, while in the third all particles mutually interact. Note that the δ-function factors must be separated out and the number of independent momentum four-vectors correspondingly reduced before one can introduce the idea of analytic continuation in energy and momentum.

3. The connected parts of S-matrix elements are analytic functions of the momenta on which they depend (these momenta being, of course, constrained to lie on the appropriate mass shells). This property together with Lorentz invariance allows the connected parts to be written as analytic functions of the scalars that can be formed from the energy-momentum four-vectors, multiplied by momentum polynomials that may depend on spin orientations. A careful discussion of this point has been given by Hepp[5] and by Barut, Muzinich, and Williams.[6] The analytic properties of connected parts are sometimes formulated in momentum space and sometimes in the space of the scalars formed from the four-vectors. We shall generally use the latter, assuming that the spin polynomials have been chosen so as to avoid the introduction of kinematical poles. The work of Barut, Muzinich, and Williams[6] and of Hearn[7] may be consulted in this latter connection, as well as Chap. 5 of Ref. 1.

4. To every particle, whether stable or unstable,[8] there is associated a family of poles on the multisheeted Riemann surface, the position of that member of the family nearest the physical region

‡A single-line connected part (→) is assigned the value unity. For the complete normalization prescription including the mass shell constraint, the reader may consult Ref. 4.

determining the mass and lifetime of the particle.‡ A given pole appears in all S-matrix connected parts that contain channels with which the associated particle can "communicate." By the term "communicating" channel we mean that if the energy were available, the particle could decay into this channel.§

The existence of particle poles is essential to the physical requirement that two successive reactions may occur with a macroscopic space-time separation. For example, one of the final neutrons in an np scattering experiment may subsequently collide with a deuteron. The over-all process $n_1 + p_1 + d_1 \rightarrow n_2 + p_2 + d_2$, described by connected-part graph,

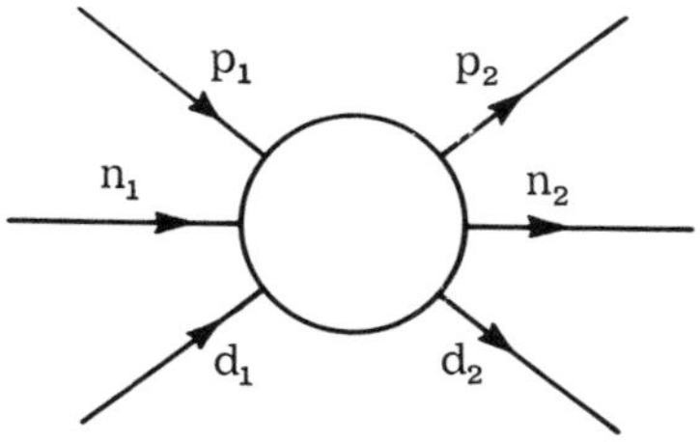

is highly improbable for most values of the energies and momenta; but if we look in the special region of the variable $(n_2 + d_2 - d_1)^2$ near m_n^2 we find an enormous enhancement due to the presence of a pole

$$\frac{\Gamma}{(n_2 + d_2 - d_1)^2 - m_n^2}$$

This pole may be represented by a graph,

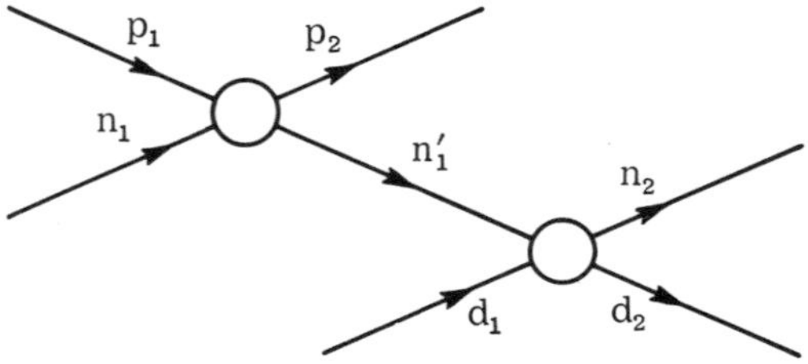

‡As first shown by Möller[8] the distance from the physical region of the nearest family member determines the inverse lifetime (or width) of the particle, so only those poles displaced by something less than 1 GeV will correspond to experimentally observable particles. A pole actually on the physical sheet corresponds to a stable particle.

§We use the term channel here in the sense of Blatt and Weisskopf ("Theoretical Nuclear Physics," Wiley, New York, 1952, Chap. VIII) rather than that of Ref. 1, where it was used synonymously with the term "reaction." For example we would say here that the reaction $a + b \rightarrow c + d$ is a transition from the channel (a,b) to the channel (c,d).

and corresponds to the possibility of the two separate and successive reactions:

$$n_1 + p_1 \rightarrow n_1' + p_2$$

followed by

$$n_1' + d_1 \rightarrow n_2 + d_2$$

Evidently such a pole must occur in every connected part whose graph contains a combination of lines having the same quantum numbers as the neutron.

5. The residue of any pole may be broken into two factors, each of which is equal to a connected part of lower dimensionality, depending only on one of the two subgroups of momenta (and spin orientations) defined by the pole graph. Thus, in our preceding example,

$$\Gamma = \Gamma_1(n_1, p_1, p_2)\, \Gamma_2(d_1, d_2, n_2)$$

Such a factorization is physically required by the independence of the two successive scatterings. In our example Γ_1 is the amplitude for np scattering and Γ_2 that for nd scattering. Note that *any* connected part may be defined as a factor in the residue of a pole of another connected part whose graph contains more lines. By this approach we can unambiguously define connected parts for unstable particles, as shown by Zwanziger[9] and by Gunson.[10]

6. Both positive and negative, real energy regions for any four-momentum in a connected part are capable of physical significance through "crossing."‡ In Chap. 2 of Ref. 1 the crossing principle was discussed for a four-line connected part, and the generalization of the idea to any number of lines will be evident. The consequence is that a single analytic function may be associated with each connected-part graph—without the necessity for specifying which lines are incoming particles and which outgoing antiparticles (or vice versa). Each graph and its associated analytic function represents all the different reactions related by crossing.

The importance of the crossing principle can hardly be overemphasized. We shall see that from it flow the dynamics of strong interactions.

7. The physical region for a particular reaction is a connected

‡We use the term "crossing" or "crossing principle" as synonymous with the substitution law. There is no implication of the symmetry arising from the presence of identical particles. The term "crossing symmetry" will be avoided here.

real domain in the momentum variables (or the scalars formed therefrom), which contains channel threshold branch points that divide the physical region into sectors. To pass from one physical sector to an adjacent sector the correct path of continuation around the dividing branch point is always into the *upper* half-plane of the variable in which the branch point occurs. This recipe, long known in simple cases and recently generalized by Olive,[4] reflects the circumstance that the S-matrix transforms an ingoing wave into an outgoing, the arrival of the former preceding the emergence of the latter in a time sense.

8. The discontinuity of an S-matrix element in passing once around a single branch point associated with the threshold of the n-th channel is given by

$$T_{ba}(1) - T_{ba}(2) = i \int_n T_{bn}(1)\, T_{na}(2) \qquad (1\text{-}1)$$

with $S = 1 + iT$. In this formula all variables are held fixed except for that one in which the branch point occurs, and the integration runs only over the n-th channel. The points (1) and (2) lie one above the other on adjacent sheets. The discontinuity recipe in this particular form is due to Cutkosky,[11] Gunson,[10] and Olive[12] and, as shown by Zwanziger[9] and Gunson,[10] may be used even for a branch point outside the physical region, the branch point corresponding to the threshold of a channel containing one or more unstable particles. Note that T_{ba} is, in general, not a connected part and contains δ-functions. These, however, can be shown to appear in a consistent way on the two sides of Eq. (1-1).[10]

The usual connection between spin and statistics has been demonstrated by Stapp to be related to the discontinuity formula and the decomposition into connected parts.[13]

9. The S matrix is unitary in physical regions. This condition, related to probability conservation and long recognized, will give certain positive definiteness properties and puts an over-all bound on the strength of singularities, as we shall see later. Stapp[14] and Olive[12] have recently emphasized that the unitarity condition is not equivalent to the discontinuity formula (1-1), as often stated. The physical content of (1-1) includes the requirement that the outgoing wave is uniquely determined by the ingoing wave, but probability conservation is not implied. Conversely, formula (1-1) can be used for branch points outside the physical region where unitarity is meaningless.

10. In addition to particle poles and threshold branch points the only other singularities are those implied by the analytic continuation of the discontinuity formula (1-1), made in accordance with principles 1-7. It has been shown by Polkinghorne[15] and Stapp[3] that these singularities may be located by the Landau prescription[16]

derived from Feynman graphs.‡ This last principle we shall call "maximal analyticity of the first degree."

An important effort is in progress by Stapp,[14] Gunson,[10] Olive,[4] and others to find a simple and clean set of axioms, closely related to experiment, that will generate the ten properties listed above and at the same time make these properties precise. As indicated at the beginning of this chapter, the current lack of precision has not prevented practical application, so on we go, hoping that the axioms to support us will be forthcoming.

‡In the graphs a line must be introduced for every pole, whether on the physical sheet or not.

2

MAXIMAL ANALYTICITY OF THE SECOND DEGREE

All ten of the S-matrix properties lised in the preceding chapter appear to be consistent with the Feynman diagram expansions of conventional field theory and to that extent do not appear to distinguish strongly interacting particles from photons and leptons. It was suggested in the Introduction that the macroscopic aspects of electromagnetism (which cannot be described through diagrams) may invalidate a general S-matrix approach for photons, apart from reactions treated superficially by the first few terms of perturbation expansions in the fine-structure constant. Since the primary interactions of the electron and muon are electromagnetic and neutrinos interact only in association with electrons and muons, it may be that a more-than-superficial S-matrix description of the leptons also is impossible. Should such be the case, it is conceivably unnecessary to add further assumptions to the ten already listed in order to achieve a self-contained theory.‡ Such a theory would encompass strong interactions but would have nothing to say about electromagnetism or weak interactions. Up to the present, however, it has not been possible to show that these ten generate the following principle that is essential to our concept of nuclear democracy: *All strong interactions are of the Yukawa type*.

By a Yukawa interaction is meant one that arises from the exchange of particles that communicate with crossed channels. It will be shown below how these forces are calculated in simple cases

---

‡Paradoxically, if the ten properties are entirely (not just superficially) compatible with the properties of leptons and photons, it seems unlikely that they could constitute a "complete" theory. Some element to distinguish the strong interactions would then be missing. The author is fully aware that this paragraph is confusing and suggests that it be reread after reaching the end of the chapter.

through the crossing principle, but it will also be shown that certain *additional* non-Yukawa interactions, corresponding roughly to "direct" absorption and emission, appear to be permitted by the ten assumptions of Chapter 1. These additional interactions characteristically single out special values of angular momentum and give a special status to particles with corresponding spins. To exclude the undemocratic non-Yukawa interactions a new principle seems needed. This principle we call "maximal analyticity of the second degree," its objective being to minimize the number of arbitrary parameters in the S-matrix, in a manner consistent with the assumptions of Chapter 1. It is generally believed that the number of poles is thereby also minimized.

Second-degree maximal analyticity has not yet been given a complete formulation but in the various approximation procedures so far proposed there is no question about how it should be applied. In other words, there never seems any doubt about the distinction between Yukawa and non-Yukawa interactions. The most promising candidate for a general formulation involves the notion of continuation in angular momentum, which has been given a precise meaning for connected parts with four lines, on the basis of the assumptions listed in Chapter 1.‡ Specifically, one may postulate that *all* the physical J values ($0, \frac{1}{2}, 1, \frac{3}{2}, \ldots$) for any four-line connected part are connected by an analytic interpolation. The requirements of Chapter 1 appear to guarantee such an interpolation for $J = \frac{3}{2}, 2, \frac{5}{2}, \ldots$, but a cloud hangs over the three lowest values, $J = 0, \frac{1}{2}, 1$.[17] With the assumption that these three values are also included in the interpolation, a big step is taken toward the elimination of non-Yukawa forces. This point will be illustrated with explicit examples in Chapters 4 and 5 involving channels where the angular momentum is entirely orbital (no spins). Whether a further assumption is needed in the general case and, indeed, whether even this assumption is required, is not yet clear.§

Reversing the logic, we shall take for granted that any satisfactory criterion for nuclear democracy guarantees a complete interpolation between all physical angular momenta of four-line connected parts. In particular all energy-momentum poles must be continuable in angular momentum, i.e., they must be Regge poles. If it could be shown that non-Regge particle poles exist, the concept of nuclear democracy would be destroyed. From an experimental standpoint no such indications have yet appeared.

---

‡Several recent books treat this subject in detail; see, for example, Ref. 17.

§Recently Gell-Mann et al. (*Phys. Letters*, 4, 265, 1963), have shown that when channels with spin are considered, an aristocratic (elementary) particle may under certain special conditions be associated with a Regge pole. It has not been shown, however, that these conditions are compatible with J-interpolation in all channels.

3

A NONRELATIVISTIC MODEL TO ILLUSTRATE MAXIMAL ANALYTICITY OF THE FIRST AND SECOND DEGREES

Let us consider a simple model, inserting a single pole in one of the reaction energies of a four-line connected part and imposing elastic unitarity and the corresponding discontinuity formula in *one* of the *other* two reactions. The problem with any finite number of poles will proceed in the same fashion, but it is an essential simplification to include only two-particle channels in the unitary condition and to impose unitarity in only one of the three reactions. (For kinematical details see Chap. 2 of Ref. 1.)

Writing the two independent variables as s and $t = -2q_S^2(1 - \cos\theta_S)$, q_S and θ_S being the barycentric system momentum and scattering angles in the s-reaction, we assume that the amplitude A(s,t) has a simple pole in t at $t = m^2$, with a constant residue $-\lambda$:

$$\lim_{t \to m^2} (m^2 - t)\,A(s,t) = \lambda$$

that is, in the corresponding potential scattering problem there would be acting in the s-reaction a Yukawa potential of range 1/m and strength λ. More generally one could say that there exists a single spin-zero elementary particle of mass m communicating with the channels of the t-reaction according to the coupling constant λ. In the s-reaction we use the nonrelativistic (N.R.) discontinuity formula [see Eq. (7-3) of Ref. 1] for a cut drawn from the threshold branch point at $q_S^2 = 0$ $(s = s_0)$ to $+\infty$:

$$\frac{1}{2i}\,[A(s^+,\theta_S) - A(s^-,\theta_S)]$$

$$= \frac{q_S}{4\pi} \int d\Omega_S\, A(s^+,\theta_S')\,A(s^-,\theta_S'') \qquad q_S^2 > 0$$

The points s^+ and s^- are just above and below the cut, respectively. It will be recognized that the conditions imposed in our model are obeyed by nonrelativistic potential scattering as given by the Schrödinger equation.

Mandelstam[18] has shown that for the above model, maximal analyticity of the first degree implies that $A(s,t)$ is an analytic function with only the single branch point in s at s_0 but a succession of t branch points at $t = 4m^2, 9m^2, \ldots$. There are no further poles in t beyond the one at m^2 but possibly poles in s. If the cuts in s and t are taken along the positive real axes to $+\infty$, one thereby defines the "physical sheet" on which the Mandelstam representation applies:

$$A(s,t) = \frac{\lambda}{m^2 - t} + \frac{1}{\pi^2} \int_{s_0}^{\infty} \frac{ds'}{s' - s} \int_{4m^2}^{\infty} \frac{dt'}{t' - t}\, \rho(s',t') + \text{possible subtraction terms} \tag{3-1}$$

Here the "possible subtraction terms" are understood to include any poles in s and single dispersion integrals (over the range s_0 to ∞), as well as the usual subtraction polynomials; also, if subtractions are necessary, the double integral must be modified to ensure its convergence. We return shortly to the subtraction terms and the arbitrary parameters which they imply, but discuss first how the t branch points of $A(s,t)$ are determined by the pole term in t.

It was demonstrated by Mandelstam[18] that, quite independently of the possible subtraction terms in (3-1), the s-channel discontinuity formula leads to the following prescription for the double spectral function (see Ref. 1, pp. 33–37):

$$\rho(s,t) = \frac{1}{2\pi q_s} \int dt' \int dt'' \times \frac{\tilde{D}^*(t',s)\,\tilde{D}(t'',s)\,\theta(K)}{K^{1/2}(s,t,t',t'')} \qquad \sqrt{t'} + \sqrt{t''} < \sqrt{t} \tag{3-2}$$

Here K is a known function and $\tilde{D}(t,s)$ is the t-discontinuity of $A(s,t)$ given by

$$\tilde{D}(t,s) = \pi\lambda\delta(m^2 - t) + \frac{1}{\pi} \int_{s_0}^{\infty} \frac{ds'}{s' - s}\, \rho(s',t) \tag{3-3}$$

If we assume that the pole at $t = m^2$ is the lowest singularity in t, these two equations determine $\tilde{D}(t,s)$ uniquely for all s and t. Thus,

$$\left.\begin{aligned}\tilde{D}(t,s) &= \pi\lambda\delta(m^2 - t) \\ \rho(s,t) &= 0\end{aligned}\right\} \begin{aligned}&\text{for all } s \\ &\text{and } -\infty < t < 4m^2\end{aligned}$$

Equation (3-2) then gives $\rho(s,t)$ in the interval $4m^2 < t < 9m^2$ and $\tilde{D}(t,s)$ is given in the same interval by (3-3). The process continues, giving $\tilde{D}(t,s)$ at any definite t after only a finite number of steps. At each stage the integral in (3-2) is over a finite region whereas that in (3-3) is convergent because of the structure of $K(s,t,t',t'')$.

This procedure illustrates the remarkable fact that the s-channel discontinuity formula plus the pole in t determines the t-channel branch points and the discontinuities across the associated cuts. Thus, first-degree maximal analyticity, which is embodied in Eqs. (3-2) and (3-3), gives a means of calculating the crossed discontinuity $\tilde{D}(t,s)$ uniquely once the "potential" (the pole in t) is known.

An important question still remains: To what extent is the amplitude $A(s,t)$ determined by its t-discontinuity $\tilde{D}(t,s)$ and the Mandelstam representation (3-1)? We write the latter as

$$A(s,t) = \frac{1}{\pi}\int_{m^2}^{\infty} \frac{dt'}{t' - t}\, \tilde{D}(t',s) + \text{possible subtraction terms} \qquad (3\text{-}4)$$

from which it is clear that our first difficulty arises in defining the integral over dt' if $\tilde{D}(t,s)$ does not approach zero for large t. It is awkward to find the behavior of $\tilde{D}(t,s)$ at large t from our dynamical equations (3-2) and (3-3); however, we know that the t-discontinuity of the Schrödinger amplitude for scattering by a Yukawa potential must also satisfy those equations, which we have shown to determine a unique $\tilde{D}(t,s)$. Using the Schrödinger equation with a Yukawa potential, Regge has shown that (see Ref. 17)

$$\tilde{D}(t,s) \underset{t\to\infty}{\sim} c(s)\, t^{\alpha_r(s)}$$

where $\alpha_r(s)$ is the trajectory of the Regge pole farthest to the right in the complex angular-momentum plane. If follows that our solution must have this form. More precisely, we can write $\tilde{D}(t,s)$ as a sum of "Regge pole" terms asymptotically proportional to $P_\alpha(\cos\theta_s)$ plus a remainder which approaches zero as a negative power as t tends to infinity, provided we include all poles in the right-half ℓ-plane.

Because $P_\alpha(z)$ contains parts which behave like z^α and $z^{-\alpha-1}$ as $z \to \infty$, it is convenient to introduce a function‡

‡We are here following the spirit of a suggestion by Khuri[19] based on formulas to be found in Bateman Manuscript Project, "Higher Transcendental Functions," A. Erdelyi, ed., McGraw-Hill, New York, 1953, Vol. 1, p. 156.

$$P_\alpha(z, z_1) = \frac{1}{\pi\sqrt{2}} \int_{z_1}^{z} \frac{dz'}{(z'^2 - 1)^{1/2}} \frac{[z' + (z'^2 - 1)^{1/2}]^{\alpha+1/2}}{(z - z')^{1/2}}$$

which can be shown to approach $P_\alpha(z)$ as $z \to \infty$ for Re $\alpha > -\frac{1}{2}$ but which behaves like $z^{-1/2}$ for Re $\alpha < -\frac{1}{2}$. The precise value of z_1 is not important, so long as it is real and greater than $1 + m^2/2q_s^2$ (for positive q_s^2). Thus we write

$$\widetilde{D}(t,s) = \pi \sum_i \beta_i(s)(2\alpha_i(s) + 1) P_{\alpha_i(s)}(1 + t/2q_s^2, 1 + m_1^2/2q_s^2)$$

$$\times\ \theta(t - m_1^2) + \widetilde{D}'(t,s) \qquad m_1^2 \geq m^2 \tag{3-5}$$

where $\alpha_i(s)$ and $\beta_i(s)$ are, respectively, the position and residue of the i-th Regge pole. It is now clear that the integral over dt' in (3-4) converges only if Re $\alpha_i(s) < 0$ for all the Regge poles. However, it is known from potential theory that all the $\alpha_i(s)$ retreat to the left-half ℓ-plane if one moves to large enough energy. Thus, given the form (3-5) at some definite energy with all poles having Re $\alpha_i \geq 0$ included, so that

$$\widetilde{D}'(t,s) \xrightarrow[t\to\infty]{} 0$$

we may increase s until all poles have moved out of the right-half ℓ-plane. But when Re $\alpha < 0$ we have

$$R_\alpha(z,z_1) = \frac{1}{\pi} \int_{z_1}^{\infty} \frac{dz'}{z' - z} P_\alpha(z',z_1)$$

$$= \frac{1}{\pi\sqrt{2}} \int_{z_1}^{\infty} \frac{dz'}{(z'^2 - 1)^{1/2}}$$

$$\times \frac{[z' + (z'^2 - 1)^{1/2}]^{\alpha+1/2}}{(z' - z)^{1/2}} \tag{3-6a}$$

which for Re $\alpha > -1$ can be shown[19] to equal

Khuri goes on to suggest that if the sum in (3-5) is extended to all Regge poles—those in the left- as well as those in the right-half ℓ-plane—the remainder function $\widetilde{D}'(t,s)$ may be reduced to zero. We do not need here such a strong assumption, however. The reader may notice that our formulas for P_α and R_α differ from Khuri's by a term $\propto (z_1 - z)^{-1/2}$; the difference is of no consequence for the arguments of this chapter but for those of Chapter 4 Khuri's original expression would conflict with unitarity in crossed channels.

$$- \frac{P\alpha(-z)}{\sin \pi\alpha} - \frac{1}{\pi\sqrt{2}} \int_{-\infty}^{\xi_1} dx \frac{\exp[(\alpha + \frac{1}{2})x]}{(\cosh x - z)^{1/2}} \tag{3-6b}$$

$$\xi_1 = \cosh^{-1} z_1$$

This latter form for $R_\alpha(z,z_1)$ may be continued to Re $\alpha > 0$. Thus we can do the integrals over the pole terms explicitly and find

$$\frac{1}{\pi} \int_{m^2}^{\infty} dt' \frac{\tilde{D}(t',s)}{t' - t}$$

$$= \pi \sum_i \beta_i(s)(2\,\alpha_i(s) + 1)\, R_{\alpha_i(s)}\,(1 + t/2q_s^2,\ 1 + m_i^2/2q_s^2)$$

$$+ \frac{1}{\pi} \int_{m^2}^{\infty} dt' \frac{\tilde{D}'(t',s)}{t' - t} \tag{3-7}$$

the value of $A(s,t)$ at the original energy being given by a simple continuation of this form. In what follows we shall use the notation of (3-4) with the understanding that when the integral diverges it is defined, by the analytic continuation procedure just given, to be (3-7).

Let us consider next the possible subtraction terms mentioned in (3-4). The function

$$\frac{1}{\pi} \int_{m^2}^{\infty} \frac{dt'}{t' - t} \tilde{D}(t',s)$$

which we have just defined through (3-7) for all s and t, is an analytic function of these variables with exactly the same singularities in t as the amplitude $A(s,t)$ itself. This means that their difference must be an entire function‡ of t. If we assume, as is generally believed, that the amplitude must be polynomial bounded, this entire function must be a polynomial of finite order. That is,

$$A(s,t) = \frac{1}{\pi} dt' \int \frac{\tilde{D}(t',s)}{t' - t} + \sum_{m=0}^{N} a_m(s)\, t^m \tag{3-8}$$

The problem is now to find the coefficients $a_m(s)$. One might suppose that substitution of (3-8) into the s-discontinuity equation would give the functions $a_m(s)$. In fact (as shown below) it gives us N real equations. We know in addition that the $a_m(s)$ are real analytic functions in the s-plane cut from s_0 to ∞. However, we shall see that

‡A function f(z) entire in z is holomorphic (analytic) in the whole finite z-plane.

such conditions are not quite sufficient to determine these functions completely. Some arbitrariness remains.

The failure of the dynamical equations (3-2) and (3-3) to determine A (s,t) completely means that maximal analyticity of the first degree does not prescribe a unique amplitude, even when we are given the pole terms in t. We may remove the ambiguous polynomial terms in (3-8) and achieve pure Yukawa scattering by a variety of equivalent assumptions, any one of which amounts in our model to maximal analyticity of the *second* degree. We may *either* (1) postulate the absence of CDD poles (see below) in the partial-wave amplitudes, (2) postulate that all phase shifts vanish at high energy, or (3) require that the partial-wave amplitude, obtained by the Froissart-Gribov continuation from physical J-values for $J > N$, should yield the actual physical amplitude for integer $J < N$.

We discuss first the possibility of CDD poles.

3–1 CDD POLES AND THE PARTIAL-WAVE AMPLITUDES

The unknown polynomials in t of Eq. (3-8) can be written as polynomials in $z = \cos\theta$, and so they clearly contribute only to partial-wave amplitudes of angular momentum $\ell \leq N$. Let us consider such an amplitude, $A_\ell(s)$. This function is real-analytic in an s-plane cut on its real axis from $-\infty$ to some s_L and from s_0 to $+\infty$ (Fig. 3-1). [Ref. 1, Chap. 10.] Its discontinuity across the left-hand (L.H.) cut is known in terms of $\widetilde{D}(t,s)$:

$$\frac{1}{2i}\underset{s \leq s_L}{\text{disc}}\; A_\ell(s) = \frac{1}{2}\int_{-1}^{+1} dz\, P_\ell(z)\, \widetilde{D}(-2q_s^2(1-z), s)$$

$$= f_\ell(s), \text{ say} \qquad (3\text{-}9)$$

This discontinuity is unambiguously determined once the poles in t have been given; it is a manifestation, in other words, of the Yukawa force. The discontinuity of A_ℓ^{-1} on the right-hand (R.H.) cut is determined by (elastic) unitarity. Since $A_\ell = e^{i\delta_\ell} \sin\delta_\ell/q_s$, we have

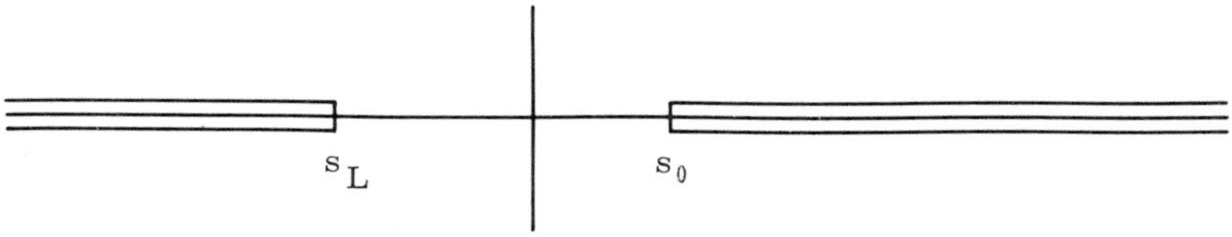

Figure 3-1

$$\text{Im } A_\ell^{-1} = -q_s \qquad s \geq s_0 \tag{3-10}$$

To get around the difficulty that Im A_ℓ is known on the left but Im A_ℓ^{-1} on the right, we use the N over D method of Wiener and Hopf.‡ This allows us to write, under quite general conditions

$$A_\ell(s) = N_\ell(s)/D_\ell(s)$$

where the R.H. cut of A_ℓ comes entirely from D_ℓ whereas N_ℓ alone has the L.H. cut. Both N_ℓ and D_ℓ are real-analytic in their respective cut planes and it follows at once that:

$$\text{Im } N_\ell(s) = f_\ell(s)\, D_\ell(s) \qquad s \leq s_L \qquad [\text{cf. Eq. (3-9)}] \tag{3-11}$$

$$\text{Im } D_\ell(s) = -q_s N_\ell(s) \qquad [\text{cf. Eq. (3-10)}] \tag{3-12}$$

The Wiener-Hopf theory ensures that this factorization of $A_\ell(s)$ is possible and that $D_\ell(s)$ can be chosen so that

$$D_\ell(s) \xrightarrow[s \to \infty]{} 1$$

Unitarity then requires that $N_\ell(s) \to 0$ as $s \to \infty$. There is no guarantee, however, that the resulting functions $N_\ell(s)$ and $D_\ell(s)$ should actually be holomorphic (i.e., have no poles) in their cut planes. In general one would expect them to have poles, although the holomorphy of $A_\ell(s)$ (apart from stable-particle poles on the real axis) does enforce some requirements on the pole positions and residues.

In potential theory it can be shown explicitly that for all ℓ both N_ℓ and D_ℓ are holomorphic. In this case a simple application of Cauchy's theorem to N_ℓ and $D_\ell - 1$, using (3-11) and (3-12) together with the real analyticity of N and D gives:

$$N_\ell(s) = \frac{1}{\pi} \int_{-\infty}^{s_L} \frac{ds'}{s' - s}\, f_\ell(s')\, D_\ell(s') \tag{3-13a}$$

and

$$D_\ell(s) = 1 - \frac{1}{\pi} \int_{s_0}^{\infty} \frac{ds'}{s' - s}\, q_{s'}\, N_\ell(s') \tag{3-13b}$$

‡This technique, as discussed, for example, in Ref. 1, Chap. 10, has been widely used by physicists during the past few years. It was, however, introduced and extensively studied by Wiener and Hopf some forty years ago. See, for example, Titchmarsh.[20]

These linear integral equations can be shown to be of the Fredholm type and to determine $A_\ell(s)$. Poles may occur in $A_\ell(s)$ through zeros of $D_\ell(s)$ but the positions and residues are determined by $f_\ell(s)$. The result is, of course, the same as obtained by solving the Schrödinger equation and is an example of dynamics governed entirely by the Yukawa force, i.e., by the poles in the crossed reaction.

By contrast, if we allow that in general N_ℓ and D_ℓ may have poles, the usual application of Cauchy's theorem gives,‡ for example, for D_ℓ

$$D_\ell(s) = 1 - \frac{1}{\pi} \int_{s_0}^{\infty} \frac{ds'}{s' - s} q_{s'} N_\ell(s') + \sum_{i=1}^{n_\ell} \frac{\gamma_\ell^{(i)}}{s - d_\ell^{(i)}}$$

where we assume that there is only a finite number, n_ℓ, of poles. These poles in D_ℓ are the so-called "CDD poles," named for Castillejo, Dalitz, and Dyson who first considered them.[21] The real analyticity of D_ℓ means that the pole terms must be real or occur in complex-conjugate pairs; also, if the associated zero is produced on the physical sheet it must come on the real axis (see below). Apart from a few such requirements§ the CDD poles are arbitrary; that is, if we try to use our knowledge of $\tilde{D}(t,s)$ to find $A(s,t)$, our dynamical equations give us no way of determining whether the poles exist or where they are. The parameters $\gamma^{(i)}$ and $d^{(i)}$ appear as arbitrary constants.

The introduction of a pole to $D_\ell(s)$ will in general produce a zero in the denominator function and thus a pole of A_ℓ which, from the known holomorphy of A_ℓ must lie on the real axis or on an unphysical sheet, corresponding either to a bound state or a resonance. Because these CDD poles in the amplitude are apparently independent of the Yukawa forces, they seem to correspond to elementary particles that communicate with the s channels, the two parameters for each pole determining the mass and the coupling constant of the associated particle.

3–2 CDD POLES AND THE ASYMPTOTIC PHASE SHIFT

Assuming that D_ℓ has only a finite number, n_ℓ, of poles and a finite number, m_ℓ, of zeros, located at $d_\ell^{(i)}$ and $c_\ell^{(i)}$, respectively, one can reconstruct $D_\ell(s)$ in terms of these poles and zeros

‡Each pole added in N_ℓ or D_ℓ will have an associated zero, so the most general situation is achieved by adding poles in D_ℓ only.

§C. Goebel has pointed out (Proceedings of the 1962 CERN Conference on High Energy Physics, p. 167) that for $\ell > 0$ the threshold requirement, $A_\ell(s) \sim q_s^{2\ell}$ as $q_s^2 \to 0$, puts a condition on CDD poles.

together with the physical phase shift. Thus, consider the Omnes function

$$\Delta_\ell(s) = D_\ell(s_0) \prod_{i=1}^{n_\ell} \frac{s_0 - d_\ell^{(i)}}{s - d_\ell^{(i)}} \prod_{j=1}^{m_\ell} \frac{s - c_\ell^{(i)}}{s_0 - c_\ell^{(j)}}$$

$$\times \exp\left\{-\frac{s - s_0}{\pi} \int_{s_0}^{\infty} \frac{ds'}{s' - s} \frac{\delta_\ell(s') - \delta_\ell(s_0)}{s' - s_0}\right\}$$

This function has the zeros and poles of $D_\ell(s)$ and has the same phase as $D_\ell(s)$ on the R.H. cut, since $A_\ell(s)$ and D_ℓ^{-1} here have the phase $\delta_\ell(s)$. Thus $D_\ell(s)/\Delta_\ell(s)$ is an entire, real-analytic function of s with no poles or zeros, i.e., a constant. Now,

$$D_\ell(s) \xrightarrow[s \to \infty]{} 1$$

whereas

$$\Delta_\ell(s) \underset{s \to \infty}{\sim} \text{const. } s^{m_\ell - n_\ell}\, s^{1/\pi\,[\delta_\ell(\infty) - \delta_\ell(s_0)]}$$

It follows that if we define conventionally

$$\delta_\ell(s_0) = m_\ell \pi$$

then

$$\delta_\ell(\infty) = n_\ell \pi$$

With scattering via Yukawa interactions only, there are no CDD poles ($n_\ell = 0$) and so, with the conventional definition of $\delta_\ell(s_0)$, we have $\delta_\ell(\infty) = 0$.

3–3 REMOVAL OF THE ARBITRARY POLYNOMIALS BY INTERPOLATION IN ANGULAR MOMENTUM

As shown above the removal of the unknown polynomial in (3-8) is equivalent to postulating that the partial-wave amplitudes have no CDD poles [or that $\delta_\ell(\infty) = 0$], that is, that $N_\ell(s)$ and $D_\ell(s)$ are holomorphic in their cut planes; for if so, they satisfy the same Fredholm-type equations (3-13) as in potential scattering and the resulting amplitude A(s,t) is precisely the Yukawa amplitude, which we know has no polynomial terms. Our characterization of CDD poles, however, depended on the elastic unitarity condition and so far has not been generalized.

An alternative prescription, pointed out by Chew, Frautschi, and Mandelstam,[22] and presented here in a modified form, has more aesthetic appeal as well as the possibility of generalization. We make the usual Froissart-Gribov analytic continuation of the partial-wave amplitude[17]

$$A_\ell(s) = \frac{1}{\pi}\int_{m^2}^{\infty} \frac{dt}{2q_s^2}\, \widetilde{D}(t,s)\, Q_\ell(1 + t/2q_s^2) \tag{3-14}$$

for Re ℓ sufficiently large, using (3-7) to obtain[19]

$$A_\ell(s) = -\sum_i \frac{2\alpha_i(s)+1}{2\ell+1}\,\frac{\beta_i(s)}{\alpha_i - \ell}\exp[-(\ell-\alpha_i)\xi_1]$$

$$+ \frac{1}{\pi}\int_{m^2}^{\infty}\frac{dt}{2q_s^2}\,\widetilde{D}'(t,s)\,Q_\ell(1 + t/2q_s^2) \tag{3-15}$$

where the sum over i includes all Regge trajectories that at any point extend into the right-half angular-momentum plane. This result then can be continued as a meromorphic‡ function of ℓ to any point, at least, in the right-half ℓ-plane. If, however, we continue to a point $\ell = n$ (integral) $< N$ we clearly do not obtain the physical partial wave $A_n(s)$ determined by the ordinary projection from (3-8), since this has the form (3-15) *plus* terms from the polynomial. The only way in which the analytically continued partial-wave amplitude can coincide with the physical amplitude at all physical values (as well as satisfy the usual uniqueness conditions[17]) is for the subtraction polynomial to be zero. All poles in s are then of the Regge type, none of the CDD type.

It has been shown by Mandelstam[23] that the N/D equations (3-13) of our model can be continued in ℓ, providing an alternative mechanism for imposing ℓ-interpolation. We shall employ such an approach below in our discussion of relativistic dynamics.

SUMMARY

We have seen that, under the conditions that A(s,t) should contain given simple poles in t and should satisfy elastic unitarity with

‡A function f(z) is meromorphic in a region if it is holomorphic there except for poles. More generally a function $f(z_1, z_2, \ldots, z_n)$ is meromorphic if it is locally the quotient of two holomorphic functions.

nonrelativistic kinematics in the s-channel, first-degree maximal analyticity determines A to within a polynomial in t. The arbitrariness corresponds to the existence of elementary particles with the quantum numbers of the s-channels. By invoking some stronger principle—no CDD poles or ℓ-interpolation—we may determine A uniquely and rule out such undemocratic particles.

In our model we in effect inserted an elementary particle into the t-channel, the two parameters of this particle determining the strength and range of the potential. In the relativistic S-matrix, however, there will be a discontinuity formula for the t-channels which will impose the same kinds of restrictions on poles in t as we have deduced above for the poles in s. In particular, if we impose angular momentum interpolation in the t-reaction, the ples in t must be of the Regge type, their positions and residues being determined by the singularities in s. There results what is called a "bootstrap" situation, the poles in s constituting the forces that produce poles in t and vice versa. Whether a consistent solution of the bootstrap problem can be found is not yet known. If it can be found there will evidently be no free parameters of the type familiar in lagrangian field theory. We shall return to such questions in Chapter 4.

4

RELATIVISTIC BOOTSTRAP DYNAMICS

There have been many attempts since 1958—when the Mandelstam representation appeared—to formulate equations within the framework of the analytically continued strong-interaction S-matrix in order to generate certain of the observed baryons and mesons on a "dynamical" basis, that is, as composites of other particles. In fact this kind of theoretical activity goes back to the early fifties and the nonrelativistic theory of the 33 resonance (now called Δ). Before the realization in 1961 of the importance of Regge poles, however, there was no serious progress with the notion that *all* baryons and mesons are composite. The obstacle to nuclear democracy was partly psychological. From the time of their discovery the nucleon and the pion were accorded a status parallel to that of the photon and the electron, respectively. It was taken for granted that the π and n masses and other properties could not be calculated but must be accepted as fundamental constants of nature.

When the possibility of Regge particle-families[17] sharing all quantum numbers except spin was proposed, however, it was immediately noticed that the nucleon (spin $\frac{1}{2}$) could be associated Regge-wise with a spin $\frac{5}{2}$ particle that clearly was not elementary. This discovery broke the spell, and attempts were then made to compute nucleon properties on a dynamical basis. The results have been sufficiently successful to convince many physicists that the nucleon is a composite state in the same sense as the deuteron. The pion still defies attempts at calculation because of its large binding energy, but the prevailing opinion now counts this only a practical difficulty.

Part of the obstacle to the concept of nuclear democracy before 1961, however, was mathematical, having to do with the asymptotic behavior of four-line connected parts. The Mandelstam representation says almost nothing about asymptotic behavior, and arbitrary subtractions (or CDD poles) corresponding to $J = 0, \frac{1}{2}$, and 1 do not appear to conflict with any of the principles of Chapter 1. For the asymptotic behavior suggested by conventional perturbation theory, furthermore, such subtractions are necessary. Subtractions for higher J produce a clear conflict,[17] so it has long been accepted that all particles with spin greater than 1 have to be composite, but at the same time it was generally believed prior to 1961 that elementary particles with low spin should exist. It was a major step forward to realize that with Regge-type asymptotic behavior *all* arbitrary subtractions might be avoided.

Actually, it has been proposed in Chapter 2 to achieve nuclear democracy not directly through an asymptotic assumption but through the postulate that all physical angular-momentum values (for each of the three reactions described by a four-line connected part) be connected by analytic interpolation. On the basis of the model discussed in the previous chapter, one expects such a postulate to preclude arbitrary subtractions, but Mandelstam has shown that there are probably branch points in angular momentum,[24] as well as poles, controlling the asymptotic behavior in momentum transfer. (These branch points arise from the interaction of the different discontinuity formulas associated with the three *different* reactions, a feature absent in the model of Chapter 3.) It is not possible, therefore, to characterize the general asymptotic situation as simply as in the model.

It seems, nevertheless, inevitable that Regge poles shall play a central role in bootstrap dynamics. The observed strongly interacting particles, stable or unstable, correspond to points on a relatively few top-ranking Regge trajectories,[17] and the problem of strong interactions can be counted as solved when we understand these top-level trajectories and the associated residues.

What accounts for the ordering and spacing of the observed trajectories? We shall show in this chapter that it appears to be a matter of crossing matrices, which determine the strength and sign of the Yukawa forces acting in any particular configuration. We restrict our attention to four-line connected parts because it is only here that the consequences of analyticity and unitarity have been extensively explored. Is it reasonable to hope that the essential features of strong interactions will be recognizable within such a restricted framework? We believe the answer to be affirmative, although the ultimate extent of progress based on two-body channels alone is not yet predictable. Our optimism is based on the presumed absence of arbitrary dimensionless constants in the strong-interaction scheme. The natural unit of energy (or mass) is $\sim$ 1 to 2 GeV, and without small or large dimensionless parameters all stable and metastable particle masses ought to be of this order of magnitude. Phase-space considerations then mean that, when stable and unstable particles are given equivalent status, most particles communicate chiefly with two-particle channels; few particles are sufficiently massive to prefer communication with channels containing three or more particles.

As a basis for our restricted discussion here we shall assume that for four-line connected parts with highly stable particles (such as pions) the Mandelstam representation is a consequence of the principles of Chapter 1. Even should this representation eventually turn out to be deficient in certain aspects, it seems plausible that most of the inferences here to be drawn from it have a substantial degree of validity. Second-degree analyticity will be imposed through angular-momentum interpolation, and it also will be assumed that the Froissart-Gribov partial-wave amplitude‡ is a meromorphic function of angular momentum, at least in the whole right-half plane. We do not, in other words, concern ourselves with the Mandelstam cuts in angular momentum that arise when channels with more than two particles are included. Finally, spin complications are ignored as before. This is consistent with our concentration on low-mass particles, which systematically have low spin.

Let us consider, to begin with, a four-line amplitude with reactions labeled as follows:

s-reaction: $a + b \rightarrow a + b$

t-reaction: $a + \bar{a} \rightarrow b + \bar{b}$

u-reaction: $a + \bar{b} \rightarrow a + \bar{b}$

The s- and u-reactions are elastic, the t-reactions may or may not be. Later we shall enlarge the discussion to arbitrary two-body reactions. The assumption that the partial-wave amplitudes are meromorphic in J in all reactions prescribes the asymptotic form of $A(s,t)$ in six directions on the usual Mandelstam plot (Fig. 4-1) in terms of the leading Regge trajectories.[17] As discussed at the beginning of Chapter 3 and in Ref. 17 it is believed that a typical leading trajectory has a behavior as shown in Fig. 4-2. (An infinite number of individually insignificant trajectories are presumed to be confined to the left-half J-plane.) The Froissart limit[25] constrains all trajectories to lie below $J = 1$ at zero total energy.

We now give the equations of Chapter 3 in the more general situation where crossing symmetry is imposed and inelastic processes occur. The Mandelstam representation for $A(s,t)$ can be written

$$A(s,t) = A_R(s,z_s) + A_L(s,z_s)$$

‡See Eq. (4-21) below. For further details see Ref. 17.

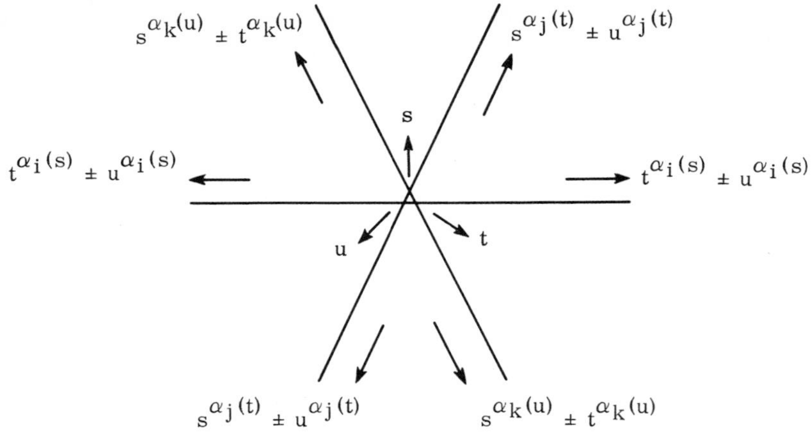

Figure 4-1

where $z_s = \cos\theta_s$, and

$$A_R(s,z_s) = \frac{1}{\pi}\int_{t_0}^{\infty} \frac{dt'}{t' - t(s,z_s)}\, D_t(t',s)$$

$$A_L(s,z_s) = \frac{1}{\pi}\int_{u_0}^{\infty} \frac{du'}{u' - u(s,z_s)}\, D_u(u',s)$$

D_t and D_u being the absorptive parts for the t- and u-channels, respectively. It is now usual to introduce two symmetrized amplitudes. $A^{\pm}(s,t)$, each having a cut only for positive $\cos\theta_s$. As discussed in Ref. 17, the Froissart-Gribov continuation in angular momentum cannot be made if there are cuts for both positive and negative $\cos\theta_s$. Remembering that

$$t = 2q_s^2 \cos\theta_s + \text{function of } s$$

whereas

$$u = -2q_s^2 \cos\theta_s + \text{function of } s$$

we define

$$A^{\pm}(s,t) = A_R(s,z_s) \pm A_L(s,-z_s) \tag{4-1}$$

Writing A as a function of s and z_s instead of s and t, it is seen that

$$A(s,z_s) = \tfrac{1}{2}[A^{+}(s,z_s) + A^{+}(s,-z_s)]$$
$$+ \tfrac{1}{2}[A^{-}(s,z_s) - A^{-}(s,-z_s)]$$

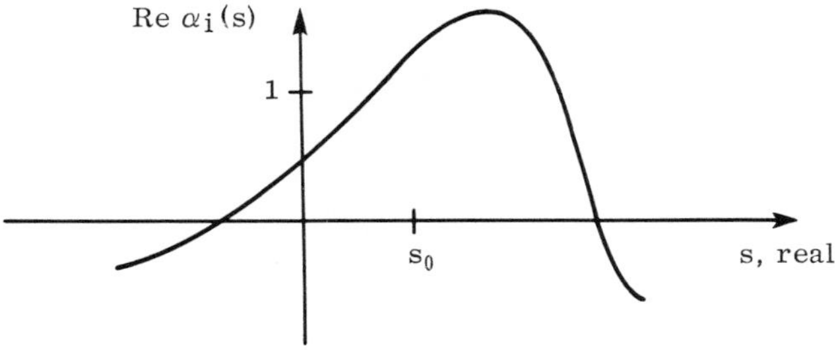

Figure 4-2

Evidently, the even part of A (in z_s) coincides with the even part of A^+, whereas the odd part of A coincides with the odd part of A^-. Note, however, that A^+ and A^- are individually neither even nor odd. When using the amplitudes $A^\pm$ we can in effect forget the presence of the u-channel whose singularities are, as it were, folded over onto the t-singularities. Thus the representation of $A^\pm$ in terms of double spectral functions becomes

$$A^\pm(s,t) = \frac{1}{\pi^2} \int \frac{ds'}{s' - s} \int \frac{dt'}{t' - t} \rho^\pm(s',t') \tag{4-2}$$

where

$$\rho^\pm(s,t) = \begin{cases} \rho_{st}(s,t) \pm \rho_{su}(s,t) & s > s_0 \\ \rho_{tu}(t,u) \pm \rho_{tu}(u,t) & s < 0 \end{cases} \tag{4-3}$$

The regions of these double spectral functions are shown in Fig. 4-3, which, since we have abandoned the symmetry between t and u, has been drawn with rectangular axes.

The form of the symmetrized amplitudes $A^\pm(s,t)$ in Eq. (4-2) is seen to be very similar to that of the N.R. amplitude discussed in Chapter 3. Apart from some kinematic factors the most obvious difference is that in the general case considered here $\rho^\pm$ has an anomalous part $\rho_A^\pm(s,t) = \rho_{tu}(t,u) \pm \rho_{tu}(u,t)$ in the region $s < 0$, where in the N.R. case $\rho = 0$.

We now split $\rho^\pm(s,t)$ into its contributions from the various s-reaction thresholds. Assuming that the process under discussion, $a + b \to a + b$, has the lowest threshold for the quantum numbers in question, the picture is much as in Fig. 4-4. Thus

$$\rho^\pm(s,t) = \rho_{el}^\pm(s,t) + \sum_i \rho_i^\pm(s,t) + \rho_A^\pm(s,t) \tag{4-4}$$

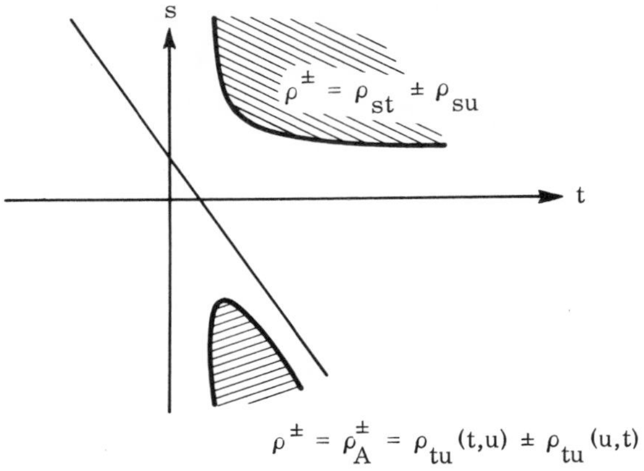

Figure 4-3

where i runs over the various inelastic channels that communicate with the s-reaction.

As before we can use the discontinuity formula to determine $\rho_{el}^{\pm}$. For the cut beginning at $s = s_0 = (m_a + m_b)^2$,

$$\frac{1}{2i}\left[A(s^+, \theta_s) - A(s^-, \theta_s)\right]$$

$$= \frac{g(s)}{4\pi} \int d\Omega_s \, A(s^+, \theta'_s)\, A(s^-, \theta''_s) \tag{4-5}$$

where $g(s) = q_s/\sqrt{s}$ is the phase-space factor. Thus, as in Chapter 3 [c.f. Eq. (3-2)] one gets

$$\rho_{el}^{\pm}(s,t) = \frac{2g(s)}{\pi q_s^2} \int dt' \int dt'' \, \frac{\widetilde{D}^{\pm *}(t', s)\, \widetilde{D}^{\pm}(t'', s)\, \theta(K)}{K^{1/2}(s,t,t',t'')} \tag{4-6}$$

an expression that can be used to define $\rho_{el}^{\pm}$ for all s. The Cutkosky graph representing this equation is shown in Fig. 4-5.

Equation (4-6) for $\rho_{el}^{\pm}$ leads one to continue the analogy with N.R. scattering and to define generalized potentials by the equation [see Eq. (3-3) as well as Chap. 7 of Ref. 1]

$$\widetilde{D}^{\pm}(t,s) = V^{\pm}(t,s) + \frac{1}{\pi} \int \frac{ds'}{s' - s} \, \rho_{el}^{\pm}(s', t) \tag{4-7}$$

where the generalized potentials $V^{\pm}(t,s)$ are given by

$$V(t,s) = \frac{1}{\pi}\int \frac{ds'}{s' - s}\left[\rho_A(s',t) + \rho_{in}(s',t)\right] \tag{4-8}$$

if

$$\rho_{in}(s,t) = \rho(s,t) - \rho_{el}(s,t) \qquad s > s_{in} \tag{4-9}$$

(We henceforth drop the ± superscripts, which carry through all these equations.)

Given the generalized potential $V(t,s)$ we know that $\tilde{D}(t,s)$ could be calculated as before by iteration, allowing the deduction of Regge trajectories and residues from its behavior at large t. Notice that now V is energy dependent (and complex for $s > s_{in}$) although in the low-energy region of certain reactions such as $NN \to NN$ one might expect this dependence to be weak. In fact by putting $V(t,s) = V(t,s_0)$ we obtain the (real and energy-independent) Charap-Fubini potential[26] given by

$$V(r) = \int dt\; V(t,s_0)\,\frac{e^{-\sqrt{t}\,r}}{r}$$

The solution of the Schrödinger equation with this potential will coincide with the solution of Eqs. (4-6) and (4-7) when s is replaced by

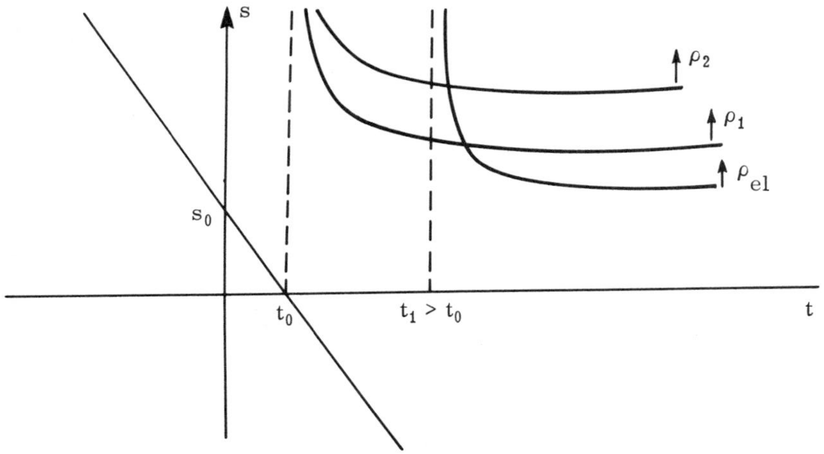

Figure 4-4

s_0 in the kinematic coefficient of (4-6) as well as in V(t,s). In general, however, these integral equations are not equivalent to a differential equation. Burke and Tate[27] have demonstrated that the iteration method is a practical one for solving Eqs. (4-6) and (4-7) but it is necessary somehow to obtain the generalized potential at the start. As might be expected, the long-range or low-t components of V(t,s) are much easier to discuss than the short-range or high-t components. Let us consider for a moment the longest-range part of the potential in order to illustrate certain elementary but crucial features of the dynamics.

The t-threshold of $\rho_{el}(s,t)$ is greater than the lowest threshold in the t-channel; e.g., in $\pi\pi$ scattering the t-threshold of the graph in Fig. 4-4 is $t_1 = 16m_\pi^2$, whereas $t_0 = 4m_\pi^2$. There is thus generally a low-t region where $V(t,s) \simeq D(t,s)$. In the elastic $\pi\pi$ problem, where all three channels refer to the same physical process, the long-range part of the potential for isotopic spin I is exactly given by (see Ref. 1, Chap. 12):

$$V_I(t,s) = \sum_{I'=0,1,2} \beta_{II'} D_{I'}(t,s) \qquad 4m_\pi^2 < t \leq 16m_\pi^2 \qquad (4\text{-}10)$$

where $\beta_{II'}$ is the crossing matrix given in Eq. (4-20) below. This relation will hold approximately up to t much higher than $16m_\pi^2$. In order to bring out some of the physical content of Eq. (4-10), suppose that there were a low-energy $\pi\pi$ resonance of isotopic spin I′ and angular momentum J_r at an energy t_r. Then for t near t_r we could put

$$D_{I'}(t,s) \approx \left(2J_r + 1\right) \text{Im}\, A_{I',J}(t)\, P_{J_r}\left(\cos\theta_t\right)$$

To make the example even more explicit, suppose that $J_r = 0$, Then, since

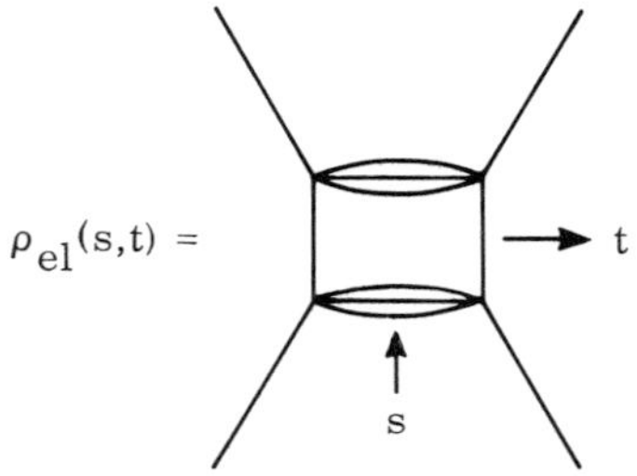

Figure 4-5

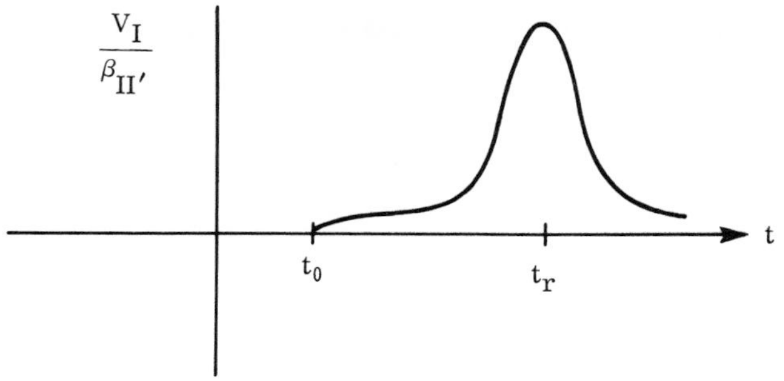

Figure 4-6

$$A_{I',J}(t) = g^{-1}(t)\, e^{i\delta_{I',J}} \sin \delta_{I',J}$$

$$V_I(t,s) \approx \beta_{II'} \frac{\sin^2 \delta_{I',0}(t)}{g(t)} \qquad t \text{ near } t_r \tag{4-11}$$

corresponding to Fig. 4-6.

We shall make three remarks about formula (4-11) for the generalized potential: (1) If the hypothetical resonance were sharp enough, $V(t,s)$ could be approximated by a δ-function in t,‡ giving us a simple Yukawa potential of range $t_r^{-1/2}$. (2) The magnitude of the coefficient of the δ-function is bounded by unitarity ($|\sin \delta| \leq 1$). (3) The sign of the coefficient is determined by the crossing matrix $\beta_{II'}$

That the potential strength cannot be arbitrarily large and that its sign is determined by symmetry considerations is a situation entirely unfamiliar in N.R. potential theory, arising from crossing and unitarity in the crossed channel. Presumably the bound on the potential is present to help ensure the Froissart limit,[25] Re $\alpha(0) \leq 1$, since we know that Re $\alpha(0)$ becomes arbitrarily large as the potential is made more and more attractive. Indeed, one may conjecture that the stability of the actual solution of the equations of S-matrix theory, where one trajectory seems to reach the ceiling set by Froissart,§ is a consequence of the unitarity limit, a circumstance sometimes described as "the principle of maximum strength for strong interactions."[22] In other words, the Yukawa forces seem to become as strong as they possibly can!

---

‡One actually *has* a δ-function when there is a stable state rather than a resonance in the t-channel, i.e., $t_r < t_0$.

§This is the so-called Pomeranchuk trajectory, belonging to the quantum numbers of the vacuum. For a full discussion, see Ref. 17.

4–1 INCLUSION OF SEVERAL TWO-BODY CHANNELS

The framework described above, including the definition of a generalized potential, can be enlarged to include an arbitrary finite number of two-body channels coupled together. We simply extend our definition of ρ_{el}, based on Fig. 4-5, to include *all* graphs with two-body states in the s direction, not simply intermediate states that coincide in type with the initial and final states. If one were discussing the KN system, for example, the $\pi\Lambda$- and $\pi\Sigma$-channels must be considered simultaneously. The formula for ρ_{el} then becomes a sum of terms of the type (4-6), involving discontinuity functions belonging to various two-body reactions. For example, the graph in Fig. 4-7 will involve the product of $D_{k\pi \to \bar{\Lambda}N}(t's)$ and $D^*_{\pi\pi \to \Lambda\bar{\Sigma}}(t'',s)$. In order to make the dynamics complete one must define a matrix generalized potential, coupling all the relevant two-body channels to each other as well as to themselves. The dynamical equations (4-6) to (4-9) are still correct provided each is understood as a matrix relation, with a dimensionality equal to the number of channels included.

In most calculations there is every reason to think that several competing two-body channels must be considered. To keep our discussion here simple, however, we shall proceed as if there were only one channel.

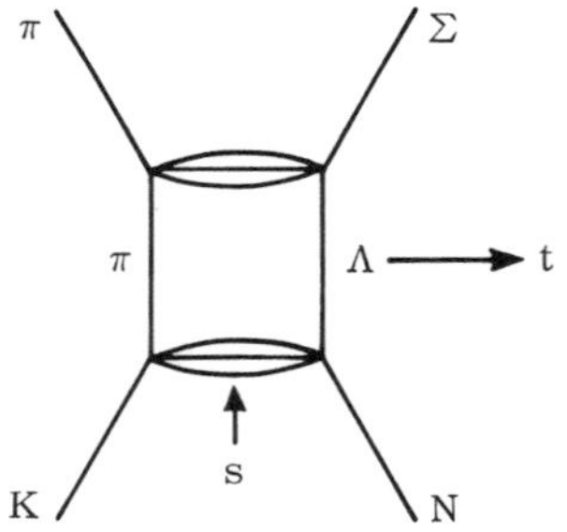

Figure 4-7

4–2 THE STRIP APPROXIMATION

In view of formula (4-11) it might seem a natural procedure to represent the effect of a zero-spin, mass m, particle known to exist with the quantum numbers of the crossed channel by a term $V(t,s) = \lambda\,\delta(m^2 - t)$, in which case one gets the problem of Chapter 3 with slightly different kinematical factors.‡ Such a procedure amounts to giving the t-channel a fixed (CDD) pole of angular momentum zero, mass m, and residue λ. It has often been used for the pion contribution to the nucleon-nucleon force. For a particle of spin J, one would have to put $V(t,s) = \lambda\,\delta(m^2 - t)\,P_J(\cos\theta_t)$ but because of the behavior§ s^J for large s it turns out to be impossible to satisfy Froissart's limit[25] if $J > 1$. Thus one cannot allow fixed poles of angular momentum greater than unity unless a cutoff is introduced. We have conjectured, of course, that all strong poles are of the Regge (moving) type, none of the CDD type.

With Regge poles the situation is quite different since although

$$A(s,t) \underset{s\to\infty}{\sim} s^{\alpha(t)} \times \text{function of } t$$

we satisfy Froissart by requiring that

$$\alpha(t) \le 1 \qquad t \le 0$$

that is, in the physical region of the s-channel the asymptotic power is less than 1 and unitarity preserved even though $\alpha(t)$ may be greater than 1 for $t > 0$. The contribution of Regge poles to the generalized potential, however, is more difficult to handle than that of fixed poles. One possible approach is through the so-called "strip approximation."[28]

The assumption of a Regge-type behavior in all reactions, with trajectories of the type shown in Fig. 4-2 means that in the usual symmetric Mandelstam plot there are six strip regions where A(s,t) may have poles on or near the physical sheet (see Fig. 4-8). So far as the pole terms go, it is the behavior of the double-spectral functions at large distances that is important; thus, to the extent that poles dominate the amplitude, the six strip regions may be considered as nonoverlapping.[29] The full amplitude may then be written

$$A(s,t,u) \approx \sum_{j=1}^{6} A_j(s,t,u) \tag{4-12}$$

where each A_j is associated with the corresponding piece of the double-spectral function. To a good approximation $A_1(s,t)$, for instance, may be taken as

$$A_1(s,t) \approx \sum_i R_i^{t_1}(s,t)$$

‡Burke and Tate[27] have succeeded in solving this kind of problem numerically, extracting the parameters of the s-channel Regge poles.

§Remember that $\cos\theta_t \sim s$ as $s \to \infty$ with t fixed.

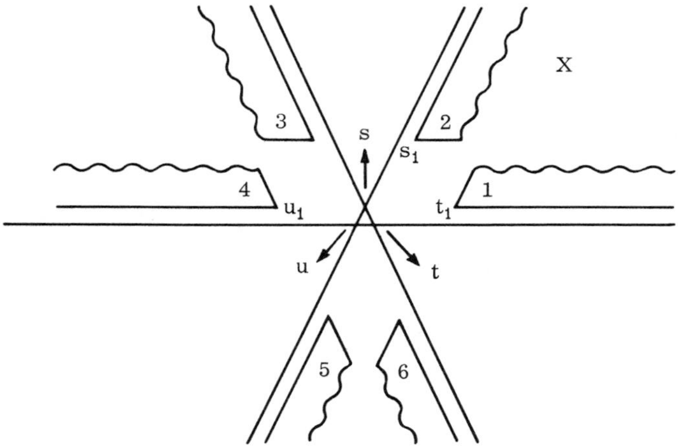

Figure 4-8

where the sum runs over all the Regge poles in the s-reaction that reach or closely approach the right-half ℓ_s-plane for some range of of s. The Regge-pole terms $R_i^{t_1}(s,t)$ are related to the functions $R_{\alpha_i}(z,z_1)$ introduced in Eq. (3-6) by

$$R_i^{t_1}(s,t) = \pi\beta_i(s)\,(2\alpha_i(s) + 1)\,R_{\alpha_i(s)}(z_s(s,t), z_s(s,t_1)) \qquad (4\text{-}13)$$

and it is shown in the Appendix that $R_i^{t_1}(s,t)$ satisfies a Mandelstam representation with a piece of double-spectral function corresponding to strip No. 1 of Fig. 4-8 although also with a spurious piece for $s < -t_1$. The spurious piece, however, should be unimportant within the spirit of the strip approximation. If desired it may be subtracted away, as shown in the Appendix.

To be quite explicit about the double-spectral function of strip No. 1, referring to formula (4-13) and the Appendix, we have for the contribution from the i-th Regge pole,

$$\rho_1^i(s,t) = \theta(s - s_0)\,\theta(t - t_1)$$

$$\times\ \mathrm{Im}\left\{\Gamma_i(s)\,P_{\alpha_i(s)}(z_s(s,t), z_s(s,t_1))\right\} \qquad (4\text{-}14)$$

where

$$\Gamma_i(s) = \pi\beta_i(s)\,(2\alpha_i(s) + 1) \qquad (4\text{-}15)$$

The precise value of the parameter t_1 (see Fig. 4-8) is not crucial, so long as it lies outside the strip for the t-channel (i.e., above the t-channel resonances). This parameter mainly affects the high angular momentum parts in the s-channel, but the contribution to large ℓ_s from strip 1 is in any event small, strips 2, 3, 5, and 6 (the "potential") dominating the peripheral collisions in the s-channel.

To see that t_1 has not much effect on the low ℓ_s values where bound states and resonances occur, let us calculate from Eq. (4-13) the portion of the ℓ-th partial wave in the s-channel arising from strip No. 1. Recalling formulas (3-15) and (3-6a), we have

$$A_1^i(s,\ell) = -\beta_i(s) \frac{2\alpha_i(s) + 1}{2\ell + 1} \frac{\exp[-(\ell - \alpha_i)\xi_1]}{\alpha_i - \ell} \tag{4-16}$$

where $\xi_1 = \log(z_1 + \sqrt{z_1^2 - 1})$ if $z_1 = z_s(s,t_1)$. When α_i is close to ℓ and we are near a bound state or resonance, it is evident that the precise value of ξ_1 (and thus of t_1) does not matter.

The question arises: Within a strip how many channels must be included in the unitarity condition? It is certainly unrealistic to hope that all resonances occur before the first inelastic threshold is reached. It is, however, theoretically plausible (as explained at the beginning of this chapter) and also experimentally indicated that only two-particle inelastic channels are appreciably open throughout the strips if we allow unstable particles to be considered. Thus, although the process $\pi + N \rightarrow 2\pi + N$ is certainly observed within the strip (i.e., within the region of πN resonances), it appears a good approximation always to consider this as $\pi + N \rightarrow \pi + \Delta$, $\pi + N \rightarrow \rho + N$, etc. If such is the case and if we can increase our ability to handle unstable particles it may be possible to avoid S-matrix elements with more than two particles in any channel. The multichannel problem, where each channel contains only two particles, is of course much easier than the general case, and as we explained above we may generalize our notion of elastic processes to include it.

Assuming that two-particle channels exhaust unitarity within the strip, as well as assuming we have the necessary ability to handle unstable particles, one could proceed as if each strip were purely elastic. In the strips 1 and 4 in Fig. 4-8 the double-spectral function would be ρ_{el} for the s-channel; in strips 2 and 5 it would be ρ_{el} for the t-channel, and so on. Strips 2, 3, 5, and 6 give the "potential" in the s-channel and correspondingly for t and u. In this way one gets a closed system of equations.

Returning to our $\pi\pi$ example, the formula for the generalized potential in the strip approximation is similar to Eq. (4-10) but instead of using the full discontinuity we omit the contributions from strips 1 and 4 in Fig. 4-8, keeping, in other words, only the Regge pole terms belonging to the crossed channels. The j-th Regge trajectory of isotopic spin I′ belonging to the t-channel gives, instead of (4-11), a term‡

$$V_I(t,s) = \beta_{II'}\left[D_2^j(t,s) + D_5^j(t,u)\right] \qquad t < t_1 \tag{4-17}$$

where

$$D_2^j(t,s) = \frac{1}{2i}\left\{\Gamma_j(t)\,R_{\alpha_j(t)}(z_t(t,s), z_t(t,s_1)) - \Gamma_j^* R_{\alpha_j^*}\right\} \tag{4-18}$$

and correspondingly for $D_5^j(t,u)$. It remains true, as can be deduced from formula (3-6b), that (4-17) behaves roughly like a δ-function near a value of $t = t_r$ for which Re α_j is equal to a physical integer, with Im α_j small; but in most cases one cannot safely replace (4-17) by a formula of the type (4-11). As emphasized earlier, such a replacement leads immediately to conflict with unitarity for a pole with $J > 1$. For $J = 0$ or $\frac{1}{2}$ and $t_r \ll t_1$, sensible results have sometimes been obtained by using (4-11) as an approximation to (4-17).

An important difficulty appears when iterating the dynamical equations with a potential of the form (4-17). Since

$$\tilde{D}(t,s) \underset{t<t_1}{=} V(t,s) \underset{s\to\infty}{\sim} s^{\alpha_j(t)} \times \text{function of } t$$

Eq. (4-6) gives for t just above t_1, remembering that $K^{1/2}(s;t,t',t'')$ and g(s) become independent of s as $s \to \infty$,

$$\rho_{el}(s,t) \underset{s\to\infty}{\sim} \iint dt'\,dt''\, s^{\alpha_j^*(t') + \alpha_j(t'') - 1}$$
$$\times \text{ function of } (t,t',t''),\ \sqrt{t'} + \sqrt{t''} < \sqrt{t} \tag{4-19}$$

contradicting the s asymptotic behavior already assumed if $\alpha_j(t')$ is larger than 1.[22] This means that ρ_{el} is not a reliable approximation to the full ρ when we move outside strip 1 (which here means $s > s_1$). Outside the strip, diagrams not included in ρ_{el} must, in fact, cancel this wrong asymptotic behavior.§ The simplest procedure is probably to ignore the ρ_{el} calculated in the region X of Fig. 4-8, relying on the assumption that the actual double-spectral function is unimportant there.

Vigorous attempts are being made at present to study the dynamics of the ππ system within the strip approximation, although the

---

‡For the "short-range" potential, $t > t_1$, further terms must be added, as shown in Ref. 28.

§Mandelstam[24] has given an explicit examole of how such a cancellation occurs.

computational difficulties, even for this simplest of all strongly-interacting systems, are formidable. The goal is to find a set of Regge trajectories and residues in the t- and u-reactions that lead (at least roughly) to potentials that generate the same trajectories in the s-channel. Qualitatively the situation is hopeful because of the structure of the crossing matrix $\beta_{II'}$ (Ref. 1, Chaps. 12 and 14):

$$\beta_{II'} = \begin{pmatrix} \frac{1}{3} & 1 & \frac{5}{3} \\ \frac{1}{3} & \frac{1}{2} & -\frac{5}{6} \\ \frac{1}{3} & -\frac{1}{2} & \frac{1}{6} \end{pmatrix} \tag{4-20}$$

We see that $I' = 0$ terms in the crossed channels give the same attractive force in all three I-spin states, whereas $I' = 1, 2$ give different forces, some attractive some repulsive. Pure attraction and the largest coefficients occur in the $I = 0$ state, so a trajectory with $I = 0$ should have the topmost rank as required by experimental observations at high energy.[17] Which trajectory will be next highest, $I = 1$ or $I = 2$? Estimates show that $I = 1$ is almost sure to win, and from this point the bootstrap mechanism begins to emerge. Suppose that the forces acting in the $I = 2$ state are too weak to raise a trajectory above $J = 0$. We may then ignore the last column of the crossing matrix and consider only forces due to $I' = 0$ and $I' = 1$ in the crossed reactions. The latter are responsible for the splitting of trajectories, being most strongly attractive for $I = 0$, half as strong but still attractive for $I = 1$, and repulsive for $I = 2$. Estimates show that these forces from (crossed) $I' = 1$ are at least as important as those due to (crossed) $I' = 0$, if the isotopic spin-1 trajectory is sufficiently high to produce the observed ρ-meson. As a consequence the isotopic spin-2 trajectory, fighting a strong repulsion from (crossed) $I' = 1$, may never reach the right-half J-plane. On the other hand, the total force acting for $I = 0$ may be so strongly attractive that it pulls not one but two trajectories into the right-half J-plane.

A quantitative realization of these hopes has not yet been achieved within the framework of Eqs. (4-6) and (4-7).‡ Because of the difficulties of using these (s,t) equations, the unitarity-analyticity problem has also been studied in the (s,ℓ) framework. Let us look now therefore at a dynamical method based on partial-wave amplitudes.

---

‡See, however, Ref. 30, where the $\pi\pi$ potential is represented by fixed $I = 1$, $J = 1$ and $I = 0$, $J = 2$ poles, rather than Regge poles, a cutoff being introduced to prevent divergences.

4–3 PARTIAL-WAVE CALCULATIONS

The usual Froissart-Gribov continuation of the partial-wave amplitude to complex ℓ may be written[17]

$$A^{\pm}(s,\ell) = \frac{1}{2\pi i} \int_{C \text{ or } C'} dz'\; A^{\pm}(s,z')\, Q_{\ell}(z')$$

$$s > s_0,\ \text{Re}\,\ell > \alpha_{max} \tag{4-21}$$

where the contours C and C′ are as shown in Fig. 4-9. The integral around C gives the familiar form

$$A^{\pm}(s,\ell) = \frac{1}{\pi} \int_{t_0}^{\infty} \frac{dt}{2q_s^2}\, \widetilde{D}^{\pm}(t,s)\, Q_{\ell}(1 + t/2q_s^2) \tag{4-22}$$

whereas that around C′ gives a form pointed out by D. Wong,[31]

$$A^{\pm}(s,\ell) = -\frac{\sin \pi\ell}{\pi} \int_{-\infty}^{-1} dz\; Q_{\ell}(-z)\, A^{\pm}(s,z)$$

$$+ \tfrac{1}{2} \int_{-1}^{+1} dz\; P_{\ell}(z)\, A^{\pm}(s,z) \tag{4-23}$$

It is possible from this last equation to infer the asymptotic behavior of $A(s,\ell)$ for large s. This is because at large energies the amplitude becomes more and more sharply peaked in the forward direction and the main contribution to the integrals in (4-23) should be from the neighborhood of $z = 1$ where $P_{\ell}(z) \approx 1$. All elastic amplitudes are believed to be dominated here by the Pomeranchuk trajectory $\alpha_P(t)$, for which $\alpha_P(0) = 1$, and we have approximately[17]

$$A(s,t) \underset{s\to\infty}{\sim} \text{constant} \times s^{1+\alpha'_P(0)t} \left(i - \cot \frac{\pi(1 + \alpha'_P(0)t)}{2}\right)$$

$$\sim \text{constant} \times s^{1+\alpha'_P(0)t} \left(i + \frac{\pi}{2}\, \alpha'_P(0)t\right)$$

for t small. Substitution into (4-23) then gives

$$A(s,\ell) \underset{s\to\infty}{\sim} \text{constant} \times \left(\frac{i}{\log s} + \frac{\pi}{2}\, \frac{1}{\log^2 s}\right) \tag{4-24}$$

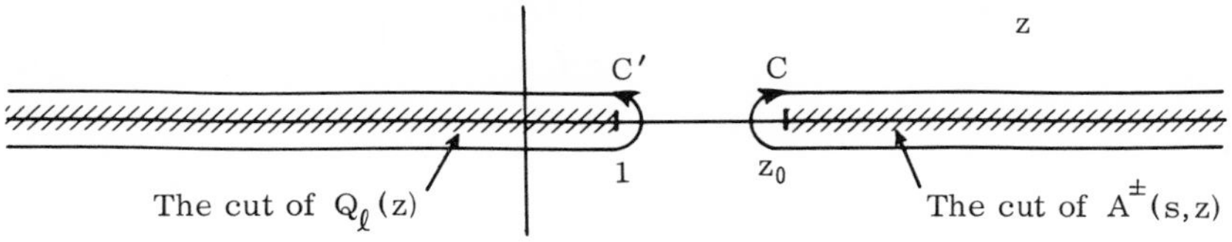

Figure 4-9

as the required limiting behavior.‡ For nonelastic amplitudes, the dominant crossed-reaction trajectory may not be the Pomeranchuk, but a corresponding calculation evidently can be carried out.

Having control of the asymptotic behavior of the partial-wave amplitude is of importance, but there remains the awkward problem of the dynamics just above the strip boundary at $s = s_1$. Inside the strip $(s_0 < s < s_1)$ we have agreed to restrict the unitarity condition to two-body configurations, but what should be done in the transition range where s is greater than s_1 but still not so large that the crossed Regge poles are completely dominant? This difficult question remains unsolved at present and, in order to proceed, the admittedly unsatisfactory assumption will be made that the imaginary part of $A_\ell(s)$ (i.e., the total cross section for the ℓ-th partial wave) is given entirely by the crossed Regge poles for *all* $s > s_1$. Thus we introduce

$$\begin{aligned} A_P(s,z_s) &= A_2(s,z_s) + A_3(s,z_s) \\ &\quad + A_5(s,z_s) + A_6(s,z_s) \end{aligned} \tag{4-25}$$

in the sense of Fig. 4-8, and define $A_P^{\pm}(s,\ell)$ to be the ℓ_s projection of $A_P(s,z_s)$ according to (4-1), (4-12), and (4-22). The subscript P is used because A_P may be thought of as the s-reaction scattering due to "peripheral" (direct) collisions. The remaining part of the amplitude, $A_1 + A_4$, can be characterized as "resonance" (indirect) scattering the s-reaction. It is, then, to be assumed that for s and ℓ real,

$$\operatorname{Im} A^{\pm}(s,\ell) = \operatorname{Im} A_P^{\pm}(s,\ell) \qquad s > s_1 \tag{4-26}$$

In so doing we completely neglect any resonance contribution to the cross section outside the strip. Undoubtedly this crude assumption

‡This limit is the same for all ℓ but the higher ℓ, the longer it takes to reach the limiting form. The asymptotic region in s for a given ℓ is characterized roughly by $s \ln s\, \alpha_P^{t\prime}(0) \gg \ell^2$.

is destined to be modified in the future, but it will allow us here to derive simple illustrative equations for Regge trajectories in the strip regions.

We use the N over D decomposition already described in Chapter 3 but modify our dynamical equations somewhat to take account of the new condition (4-26). Further to simplify the problem we also assume for s and ℓ real,

$$\text{Im } B^{\pm}(s,\ell) = \text{Im } B_P^{\pm}(s,\ell) \qquad s < s_0 \tag{4-27}$$

where $B^{\pm}(s,\ell) = q_S^{-2\ell} A^{\pm}(s,\ell)$.[17] This condition can be shown to be exact for $-t_1 \leq s < s_0$; the "resonance" terms A_1 and A_4 give partial-wave amplitudes with left-hand cuts beginning only at $q_S^2 = -t_1/4$, whereas the cuts in the peripheral terms begin already at $q_S^2 = -t_0/4$. For $s < -t_1$ we are outside the s-reaction strip and, although the resonance terms do have imaginary parts here, they should be weak compared to the peripheral terms. Asymptotically, as $s \to -\infty$, Eq. (4-27) becomes exact, just as does (4-26) when $s \to +\infty$.

Our problem is to find a real analytic function $B(s,\ell)$ that approaches $B_P(s,\ell)$ for large s (we now drop the ± superscripts) and whose cuts and discontinuities are the same as $B_P(s,\ell)$ except for the (physical) interval $s_0 \leq s \leq s_1$, where we use the two-body unitarity conditions (s and ℓ both real)‡

$$\text{Im } B(s,\ell) = B^*(s,\ell)g(s,\ell)B(s,\ell) \tag{4-28}$$

Writing

$$B(s,\ell) = N(s,\ell)\, D^{-1}(s,\ell)$$

(4-28) becomes

$$\text{Im } D(s,\ell) = -g(s,\ell)N(s,\ell) \qquad s_0 \leq s \leq s_1 \tag{4-29}$$

if we take $N(s,\ell)$ real in this interval. Let us now define $D(s,\ell)$ to be real except for this finite cut and then from (4-26) and (4-27),

$$\text{Im } N(s,\ell) = \text{Im } B_P(s,\ell)\, D(s,\ell) \qquad s < s_0 \text{ and } s > s_1 \tag{4-30}$$

At this point we may write down dispersion relations and it is convenient as before to normalize D to unity at $s = \infty$:

---

‡With more than one two-body channel all our equations, including (4-28), are to be interpreted as matrix relations in the manner described by Bjorken.[32]

$$D(s,\ell) = 1 - \frac{1}{\pi} \int_{s_0}^{s_1} ds' \frac{g(s',\ell) N(s',\ell)}{s' - s} \tag{4-31}$$

The function $N(s,\ell) - B_P(s,\ell)D(s,\ell)$ then vanishes at infinity and, in view of (4-30), has only the cut between s_0 and s_1. Thus

$$N(s,\ell) - B_P(s,\ell) D(s,\ell) = -\frac{1}{\pi} \int_{s_0}^{s_1} ds' \times \frac{\mathrm{Im}\,\{B_P(s'\ell)\, D(s',\ell)\}}{s' - s} \tag{4-32}$$

equations which when combined, and use is made of (4-29), lead to

$$N(s,\ell) = B_P(s,\ell) + \frac{1}{\pi} \int_{s_0}^{s_1} \frac{B_P(s',\ell) - B_P(s,\ell)}{s' - s} \times g(s',\ell)N(s',\ell) \tag{4-33}$$

Also used here is the fact that $B_P(s,\ell)$ is real for $s_0 < s < s_1$, which follows from the corresponding reality in this region of $A_P(s,z_s)$ as given by Eq. (4-25)

Equation (4-33) can be shown to be of the Fredholm type and thus the solutions have the same analyticity properties in ℓ as the peripheral term $B_P(s,\ell)$, except for possible fixed poles in ℓ when the Fredholm determinant vanishes. Any such poles would also occur in $D(s,\ell)$, however, and so cancel out in the quotient $B = N/D$. The only singularities of $B(s,\ell)$ in the region of holomorphy of $B_P(s,\ell)$, therefore, are Regge poles arising from the zeros of $D(s,\ell)$. Inspection of the peripheral term $B_P(s,\ell)$ shows it to be analytic in ℓ for the entire right-half ℓ-plane provided that the residue functions $\Gamma^i(t)$ and $\Gamma^i(u)$ [see formula (4-15)] for the crossed poles all vanish for high argument at least as fast as a negative power. Such a vanishing occurs for nonrelativistic potential scattering and is required if the strip approximation is to make sense. It can be shown to be a property of residues arising from the approximate equations (4-33) and (4-31)[28]; to this extent we have a self-consistent situation within the strip approximation.

To summarize the bootstrap problem as it has been formulated here for partial waves, we try to find a set of top-ranking trajectories and residues for the three reactions that are self-consistent in the following sense: the poles of the t- and u-reactions furnish the Yukawa forces [via $B_P(s,\ell)$] that generate the poles of the s-reaction [i.e., zeros of $D(s,\ell)$] through Eqs. (4-32) and (4-33). In the same way the poles of the s- and u-reactions must generate the poles of the t-reaction, whereas the s,t poles support those of u. If all strip widths s_1, t_1, etc., are set equal then this parameter determines the energy scale when the scope of the calculation is extended to trajectories containing the external particles. Naturally, many less ambitious calculations have been and will be tried where external masses are accepted as given. In such cases the strip width appears as an adjustable parameter.

It will manifestly be impossible to find completely self-consistent poles in the strip approximation. All we can ask is for rough self-consistency across the strips. Improvement can be made in the crude conditions (4-26) and (4-27),‡ but it seems unlikely that a mathematically self-consistent approximation can ever be achieved in a system lacking variable dimensionless parameters. The degree of consistency to be sought in practice is still obscure.

Also obscure is the possibility of more than one roughly self-consistent solution to our ferociously nonlinear system, but for the present such a question is entirely academic. Implementation of even the crude equations described in this chapter with given external masses and spins, still lies in the future, although the difficulties seem to be only of a computational nature if consideration is restricted to stable external particles with spin less than 1. Higher external spin and instability promise to involve major additional complications.

4—4 CURRENT ACHIEVEMENTS IN DYNAMICAL CALCULATIONS

Although no results can yet be reported on solutions of Reggeized bootstrap equations, there are grounds for optimism in results from related but less difficult calculations. For example, it has seemed probable since the 1955 work of Chew and Low that the Δ-particle may be regarded in first approximation as a pion-nucleon composite held together by exchange of a nucleon. In the language of this chapter, such a statement means that if the s-reaction is $\pi + N \rightarrow \pi + N$, the t-reaction $\pi + \bar{\pi} \rightarrow N + \bar{N}$, and the u-reaction $\bar{\pi} + N \rightarrow \bar{\pi} + N$, then for isotopic spin $\frac{3}{2}$, even parity, and J-signature corresponding to physical $J = \frac{3}{2}, \frac{7}{2}, \ldots$ in the s-reaction, the crossing matrix leads to a large and predominantly positive contribution from the nucleon trajectory in the u-reaction, with relatively weak contributions from the other trajectories. This attractive force is supposed to sustain the Δ trajectory in the s-reaction. Since the nucleon has a low spin ($\frac{1}{2}$), one may try to replace the effect of the associated Regge trajectory by a fixed pole, and recent calculations based on pre-Regge N/D techniques have led to semiquantitative success in understanding

‡See, for example, Ref. 28.

the mass and width of the Δ in terms of the nucleon and pion masses and the residue of the nucleon pole in the u-channel.[33] A similar approach explains the nucleon trajectory as principally due to attractive Yukawa forces arising from crossed Δ and nucleon trajectories in the πN reaction, as well as the ρ trajectory in the $\pi\pi$ or N$\bar{\text{N}}$ reaction.[33]

The favorable auguries in the $\pi\pi$ crossing matrix for understanding trajectories with the quantum numbers of 2π systems have already been pointed out, and qualitative success in understanding the mass and width of the ρ in terms of the π mass has been reported by Zachariasen[34] and by Balazs.[35] Inclusion of the $\pi\omega$ as well as the $\pi\pi$ channel in a matrix N/D calculation has been studied by Zachariasen and Zemach.[36] Crossing matrices also seem favorable to an understanding of several other particles as predominantly simple two-body composites.‡

If crossing matrices are indeed the key to which particles exist, then the underlying symmetries are inextricably involved in the bootstrap mechanism. It may turn out, as mentioned in the Introduction, that the only set of symmetries capable of permitting a self-consistent strong-interaction S-matrix without arbitrary (CDD) poles is the set we observe. In such an event a breakthrough on the group theoretical level might make detailed dynamical calculations unnecessary for verification of the essential elements of bootstrap theory; nevertheless the desire for a quantitative understanding of at least a few particle masses and widths seems likely to persist. In this concluding chapter, two possible schemes for dynamical bootstrap calculations have been described, but others are also being studied. It is too soon to pick out one scheme as being obviously superior.

There has been no hint yet from S-matrix calculations of any obvious flaw in the bootstrap idea and the associated picture of a nuclear democracy. At some point, of course, a flaw must develop if a connection is to be made with electromagnetism and weak interactions. As indicated in Chapters 1 and 2, however, this puzzle may be associated with the difficulty of achieving a coarse-grained space-time from strong interactions alone. Should such a deep consideration be at the root of the difficulty, we can count on a lengthy period of fun with the bootstrap.

‡See, for example, Ref. 37.

APPENDIX: ANALYTICITY PROPERTIES OF THE MODIFIED KHURI-JONES FORMULA

APPENDIX: ANALYTICITY PROPERTIES OF THE MODIFIED KHURI-JONES FORMULA

It will here be shown that the function [see formula (3-6a)]

$$R_i(s,t) = \pi\beta_i(s)(2\alpha_i(s) + 1)R_{\alpha_i(s)}(z_s(s,t), z_s(s,t_1)) \tag{A-1}$$

satisfies a Mandelstam representation in s and t, and we shall determine the boundaries of its double-spectral function. Using the notation $\lambda_i(s) = \alpha_i(s) + \frac{1}{2}$ and $\gamma_i(s) = q_s^{-2\alpha_i(s)}\beta_i(s)$ and remembering that $z_s = 1 + t/2q_s^2$, (A-1) may be rewritten from (3-6a) in the form

$$R_i(s,t) = \lambda_i(s)\gamma_i(s)\int_{t_1}^{\infty} \frac{\left\{q_s^2 + t'/2 + \sqrt{t'(q_s^2 + t'/4)}\right\}^{\lambda_i(s)}}{(t' - t)^{1/2}} \times \frac{dt'}{\sqrt{t'(q_s^2 + t'/4)}} \tag{A-2}$$

For any fixed values of s it is seen that there is a cut in t from t_1 to ∞, and 1/2i times the discontinuity across this cut is [see formula (3-5)]

$$\begin{aligned} D_i(t,s) &= \theta(t - t_1)\lambda_i(s)\gamma_i(s) \times \int_{t_1}^{t} \frac{\{q_s^2 + t'/2 + \sqrt{t'(q_s^2 + t'/4)}\}^{\lambda_i(s)}}{(t - t')^{1/2}} \times \frac{dt'}{\sqrt{t'(q_s^2 + t'/4)}} \\ &= \theta(t - t_1)\pi\beta_i(s)(2\alpha_i(s) + 1)P_{\alpha_i(s)}(z_s(s,t), z_s(s,t_1)) \end{aligned} \tag{A-3}$$

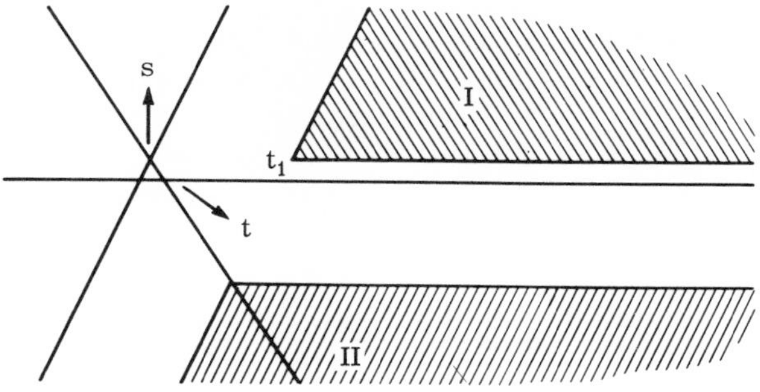

Figure A-1

an analytic function of s real in the gap between $q_s^2 = 0$ and $q_s^2 = -t_1/4$. It follows that $R_i(s,t)$ satisfies a Mandelstam representation. There are two double-spectral regions, with straight line boundaries as shown in Fig. A-1. The upper region (I) is associated with the physical s-cut in $\lambda_i(s)$ and $\gamma_i(s)$, whereas the lower (II) is associated with the vanishing of the square root $t'(q_s^2 + t'/4)$ appearing in the integrand of (A-3).

Provided that the Regge coefficient $\Gamma_i(s)$ [see formula (4-15)] goes to zero as $s \to -\infty$ at least as fast as a negative power, there is no impediment to subtracting out the contribution from region II, defining

$$R_i'(s,t) = R_i(s,t) - \frac{1}{\pi} \int_{II} ds' \, \frac{D_i^a(s',t)}{s' - s} \tag{A-4}$$

where $D_i^a(s,t)$ is the analytic continuation in t of

$$\theta(-q_s^2 - t_1/4) \; \mathrm{Im}\, R_i(s,t) \qquad t \text{ real and } > t_1$$

Explicitly,

$$D_i^a(s,t) = \theta(-q_s^2 - t_1/4)\,\lambda_i(s)\,\gamma_i(s)$$

$$\times \int_{t_1}^{-4q_s^2} \frac{dt'}{(t' - t)^{1/2}}$$

$$\times \; \mathrm{Im} \, \frac{\left\{q_s^2 + t'/2 + \sqrt{t'(q_s^2 + t'/4)}\right\}^{\lambda_i(s)}}{\sqrt{t'(q_s^2 + t'/4)}} \tag{A-5}$$

Inspection of (A-5) shows that $D_i^a(s,t) \propto \lambda_i(s)\gamma_i(s)s^{\alpha_i(s)}$ ln s $\propto$ $\Gamma_i(s)$ ln s as s $\to -\infty$, so the integral in (A-4) exists if $\Gamma_i(s)$ vanishes asymptotically faster than some negative power. Subtraction of the unwanted cut in s does not change the analyticity properties or asymptotic behavior in t.

REFERENCES

REFERENCES

1. G. F. Chew, "S-Matrix Theory of Strong Interactions," Benjamin, New York, 1961.
2. E. P. Wigner, The Role of Invariance Principles in Natural Philosophy, Varenna lecture, 1963.
3. H. P. Stapp, *Phys. Rev.,* **125,** 2139 (1962).
4. D. Olive, An Exploration of S-Matrix Theory, Carnegie Institute of Technology preprint, 1964.
5. K. Hepp, Lorentz invariant analytic S-Matrix amplitudes, ETH preprint, Zurich, 1963.
6. A. O. Barut, I. Muzinich, and D. N. Williams, *Phys. Rev.,* **130,** 442 (1963); D. N. Williams, Construction of Invariant Scalar Amplitudes without Kinematic Singularities for Arbitrary Spin Non-Zero Mass Two-Body Scattering Amplitudes, Thesis, University of California, Berkeley, 1963.
7. A. C. Hearn, *Nuovo Cimento,* **21,** 333 (1961).
8. C. Möller, *Kgl. Danske Videnskab. Selskab, Mat. Fys. Medd.,* **22,** 1 (1946); H. P. Stapp, UCRL-10261, Berkeley (1963).
9. D. Zwanziger, *Phys. Rev.,* **131,** 888 (1963).
10. J. Gunson, Unitarity and on mass shell analyticity as a basis for S-matrix theories, University of Birmingham preprint, 1962.
11. R. E. Cutkosky, *J. Math. Phys.,* **1,** 429 (1960).
12. D. Olive, *Nuovo Cimento,* **29,** 326 (1963).
13. H. P. Stapp, UCRL-10289, Berkeley (1962).
14. H. P. Stapp, "Proceedings of the 1963 Midwest Conference on Theoretical Physics," p. 199, Univ. of Notre Dame.
15. J. C. Polkinghorne, *Nuovo Cimento,* **23,** 360 (1962; ibid., **25,** 901 (1962).
16. L. D. Landau, *Nuclear Phys.,* **13,** 181 (1959).
17. E. Squires, "Complex Angular Momenta and Particle Physics," Benjamin, New York, 1963; M. Froissart and R. Omnès,

"Mandelstam Theory and Regge Poles," Benjamin, New York, 1963; S. Frautschi, "Regge Poles and S-Matrix Theory," Benjamin, New York, 1963.
18. S. Mandelstam, *Phys. Rev.*, **112**, 1344 (1958).
19. N. Khuri, *Phys. Rev.*, **130**, 429 (1963).
20. E. Titchmarsh, "Introduction to the Theory of Fourier Integrals," Clarendon Press, Oxford, 1948, p. 339.
21. L. Castillejo, R. Dalitz, and F. Dyson, *Phys. Rev.*, **101**, 453 (1956).
22. G. F. Chew, S. C. Frautschi, and S. Mandelstam, *Phys. Rev.*, **126**, 1202 (1962); G. F. Chew and S. C. Frautschi, *Phys. Rev. Letters*, **7**, 394 (1961); ibid., **8**, 41 (1962).
23. S. Mandelstam, *Ann. Phys. (N.Y.)*, **21**, 302 (1963).
24. S. Mandelstam, *Nuovo Cimento*, **30**, 1148 and 1127 (1963).
25. M. Froissart, *Phys. Rev.*, **123**, 1053 (1961).
26. J. Charap and S. Fubini, *Nuovo Cimento*, **14**, 540 (1959).
27. P. Burke and C. Tate, in "Proceedings of the 1962 International Conference on High Energy Physics," CERN, p. 507.
28. G. F. Chew and C. E. Jones, UCRL-10992, Berkeley, 1963.
29. G. F. Chew, *Phys. Rev.*, **129**, 2363 (1963).
30. B. H. Bransden, P. G. Burke, J. W. Moffat, R. G. Moorhouse, and D. Morgan, *Nuovo Cimento*, **30**, 207 (1963).
31. D. Wong, private communication, 1962.
32. J. D. Bjorken, *Phys. Rev. Letters*, **4**, 473 (1960).
33. G. F. Chew, *Phys. Rev. Letters*, **9**, 233 (1962); V. Singh and B. M. Udgaonkar, *Phys. Rev.*, **130**, 1177 (1963); E. Abers and C. Zemach, *Phys. Rev.*, **131**, 2305 (1963); J. Ball and D. Wong, *Phys. Rev.*, **133**, B179 (1964); S. Frautschi and D. Walecka, *Phys. Rev.*, **120**, 1486 (1960).
34. F. Zachariasen, *Phys. Rev. Letters*, **7**, 112 (1961).
35. L. Balazs, *Phys. Rev.*, **128**, 1939 (1962); ibid., **129**, 872 (1963).
36. F. Zachariasen and C. Zemach, *Phys. Rev.*, **128**, 849 (1962).
37. D. Neville, *Phys. Rev.*, **132**, 844 (1963).

INDEX